LIFE OF QI
THE SCIENCE OF **LIFE FORCE**

DAVID WONG

Copyright © 2022 David Wong

USA Edition, June 2022, manufactured in USA

ISBN: 978-1-7364204-1-6

A Qi Life Publication. First published in Canada, 2022.

Visit www.UseTheQi.com to learn more.

To shop Qi Life products, visit www.QiLifeStore.com today.

DISCLAIMER

to my wife...

CONTENTS

LIFE OF QI

IMAGINE...
A HEALING FUTURE

David Wong, author of this book, practicing Qigong.

magine detecting an illness *before* it becomes problematic. Imagine a world where you are no longer prescribed pharmaceuticals, but instead, prescribed targeted frequencies with zero side effects. Imagine surgery being a thing of the past, replaced by non-invasive, energy wavelengths that can reatomize internal problems without the use of a scalpel. Imagine broken bones and internal wounds being healed instantly. Imagine chronic pain and thousands of other ailments being eliminated at the source—at the cellular and molecular level. Imagine artificial intelligence being able to do all of this automatically for you, to keep you healthy every minute of the day, tracking your health status, and sending you the precise frequencies you need in order to maintain peak performance. Imagine being recharged and receiving micro-doses of frequencies through a device that you can wear, or a bed that you can sleep on each night. Imagine only needing a physician in the absolute worst-case emergencies.

Now imagine all of those possibilities being affordable, sustainable, and accessible to all. Sounds too good to be true, doesn't it? What if I told you that's exactly where the science is taking us? What if I told you that horizon is closer than you think?

What benefits might such a future bring with it? To begin with, the human experience will become far less complicated. At long last, we will enjoy a health-span to go along with our increased lifespan. Getting older will no longer mean such a steep spiral in decline. We'll be able to better regulate the process of aging, making it more dignified, comfortable, and active. We'll open new neural pathways by hacking our biology, enabling cures to some of our most pressing degenerative and neurological conditions; autism, Alzheimer's, dementia, epilepsy, depression, and more…. These will all become things of the past. We'll go even further though. Using that same neural pathway expansion, we'll enhance human cognition, bringing about new intellectual and creative abilities, transforming the way we approach education and lifelong learning. We'll transcend the limitations of our minds, access the full abilities of our brain's power, and achieve new states of consciousness. We'll eradicate devastating diseases like cancer, diabetes, heart disease, and more, by tuningour cellular structures. We'll supercharge healing by cellular regeneration.

All of this will become possible with the exponential advancement of information and science that is upon us. This version of tomorrow will come to be through the powers of resonant energy… frequency.

Scientists call this 'energy medicine'. I call it Qi Energy. The secret of this life force (of the universe's cosmic, subtle energy) can improve our lives in ways that will leave you in awe. In these pages, I'll tell you how I found myself drawn to this scientific revolution, how it changed my life, and how it will change yours, too. You'll discover an abundance of opportunity, advancement, and transformation. What was once considered ancient myth is now scientific fact. You already have the source energy of this cosmic potential encoded into your DNA. Masters of energy have known this secret for generations. And now it's our turn to harness its power. Join me as we begin our journey in the *Life of Qi…*

ENERGY TRAVELS

HOW A QIGONG MASTER STOPPED CANCER FROM 3,000 MILES AWAY

n traditional Chinese medicine, dating back more than 3.000 years, an energy force known as Qi has been said to form the basis of life. It is life force itself. Its two polarities, yin and yang, are at constant odds. Its balance brings health. Its imbalance brings disease. Balancing these odds then is both an art form and a precise spiritual science. In this way, understanding Qi is actually quite simple, but mastering its balance is a real skill that takes intense training and focus. This mastering can be referred to as Qigong—in essence, the control and manipulation of Qi's flow, both inside and outside the body.

For centuries, the secrets of Qigong masters remained elusive and mysterious. Like the shaman of so many cultures and civilizations, the masters possess an exceptional selection of abilities, wisdom handed down from master to master. It wasn't until the late 1970s that scientific research into Qigong mastery began to develop. By the mid-1980s, more than fifty research papers exploring the effects of Qi energy flow had been published. Since then, many dozens more have followed.

The practice of Qigong combines concentration, meditation, visualization, movement, and biofeedback to command the flow of Qi and direct it where it needs to go to enable the best form of balance and harmony. This balance can be achieved in various forms: cognitive, physical, spiritual, moral, medical, and more.

And it is this last form, medical, that is proving increasingly exciting in research facilities around the world. In 2002, Dr. Kevin Chen, of the University of Maryland, reviewed dozens of Qigong cancer studies carried out by Chinese researchers. He concluded that patients who underwent Qigong therapies "showed more improvement or had a better survival rate than conventional methods alone." (Chen, 2002) This sort of therapy is known as 'energy healing'.

In fact, some studies have shown that Qigong energy healing can be conducted without the practitioner and the patient being in the same place at all. In 2008, Penn State University's Professor John Neely published a scientific paper that detailed something positively extraordinary. In collaboration with renowned Qigong master Jixing Li, Neely documented longdistance energy transmission targeted with virtual pinpoint accuracy. Master Li was located in California, while Dr. Neely's lab was in Pennsylvania. Over the course of several experiments, Neely placed human sarcoma cancer cells in various laboratory incubators. Some were used as controls and others were to be targeted directly by Li's Qi energy— from the other side of the continent! In some cases, the samples and the controls were placed in separate rooms in Neely's lab. In others, they were placed close to one another, even on separate shelves in the same room. This was to test the accuracy of Master Li's energy transmission. The goal was for Li to avoid affecting the control samples even when they were placed close to the target samples.

Growth in Control Incubator, initial time period. Treatment energy is being sent to the other incubator, thetreatment incubator, during this time period. Note exponential growth, which is expected. *Courtesy of Dr. John Neely.*

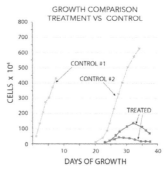

Growth in Treatment Incubator. Note that treatment begins on day 21. The samples in the treatment incubator which were targeted show reduced in growth. Control #2 is inside the treatment incubator, but was not targeted. Its growth curve appears normal. *Courtesy of Dr. John Neely.*

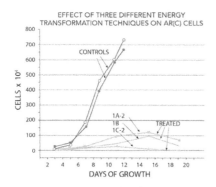

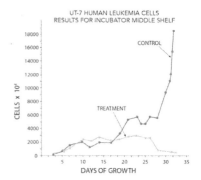

Figure 0.2 (*Source: Swanson, 2003, license unknown*)
Graphs provided by Dr. John Neely showing the effects of
long-distance energy healing carried out by Master Jixing Li.

The results across this series of experiments were astounding. From a distance of 3,000 miles across North America, Master Li could repeatedly target his Qi energy on the desired samples without affecting the control incubators. The control cell samples continued to grow exponentially, while the target cell samples diminished and died. In later experiments, the sarcoma cells were replaced with leukemia cells, which are even harder to treat with conventional pharmaceutical solutions. After a month of Master Li transmitting his Qi energy across the continent, the leukemia cells were dead, too. Dr. Neely would later say, "This is a breakthrough in biological science. It shows that changing the primary energy structure of cells can change their characteristics." (Neely, 2009)

These tests substantiate that the laws of physics can be bent to our will, that when subtle energies are harnessed and focussed by tuned masters, precision healing can be successfully achieved, even across great distances. They showcase that modern medicine can be aided by, and in some cases even replaced by, traditional healing practices.

This is the power of Qi. This is the power of subtle energy. If we're brave enough to take advantage of these ancient secrets, the future of medicine and healing can be transformed forever.

CHAPTER 1

MY JOURNEY TO A QI LIFE

t was cold that day—the day I fell three stories to the ground. A long way down for a nine-year-old. A long way down for anyone, really. Perhaps my heavy winter jacket cushioned my landing. It sure didn't feel like it though. Cement is cement after all. There's only so much cushioning a few down feathers can offer from such a height. It was my fault, too. That's what bothers me looking back. I'd been playing along a railing after school. Leaning over the top bar, balancing on the middle one, feeling gravity tug at me ever so slightly. Foolish, yes, but then, it's okay to be foolish now and then. Sometimes the risk is worth it. Sometimes it's not. Maybe the backpack I had on tipped the scales and made me a little top-heavy. Who's to say? There's no way to know at this point. I just fell. That's all. I remember the whoosh of cold air rushing over my exposed cheeks when gravity finally won out. Down I went, head first. And then nothing. Just an impact I can't recall. A quick fade to blackness tucked far in the shadows of my memory. I can still feel that darkness: an inky black infinity. It felt like I was floating, deprived of any sensory input. I could sense my own existence, but even *that* felt distant somehow. And then the light crept back in. My eyes fluttered open. And there they were...

Someone or *something* must have been looking over me that day. Some other students found me there not long after, face down in a pool of my own blood. I probably gave them quite the scare. I don't think I screamed as I fell, so I'm not sure how long after the impact they found me. It was a good thing they did though. I was hurt very badly. I looked like I'd lost a fight with the biggest, toughest bully at school. I was speaking Cantonese when I came to, the sort of bizarre thing you read about in a newspaper. I still wonder what I said. I can just barely remember staring up at them, all bent down over me, like in a movie. Their heads formed a semi-circle of round shadows above me, set against the bright blue sky. I could barely make any of their faces out, but I remember the clouds beyond them. Giant wisps of white racing by as if the world had started spinning faster. The kids were confused, and one rushed off to find a teacher who could speak Chinese back to me, unsure how best to help. This was before every kid on the playground had a cell phone in their pocket, so calling 9-1-1 right away wasn't the first thing that crossed their minds. Not that it mattered. An ambulance was called soon enough, and I was quickly off to an intensive care unit regardless of which language was coming from my lips. I had always wanted to ride in an ambulance... but not like that. The passenger seat as a ride-along would have been a much more enjoyable experience. Even still, I remember the sirens blaring as we sped through town. They were muffled and came in and out each time I lost consciousness and woke again. There was a paramedic in the back with me. He kept saying it was going to be all right.

I was in surgery for about an hour after arriving at the hospital. I had broken my neck, and my skull was fractured in multiple places. I had lost a lot of blood, and there was internal bleeding as well. They were forced to top me up with a donor infusion to make up for what I'd lost back on the playground. The initial X-rays showed that the fractures in my skull had resulted in bone fragments, so they removed them during the surgery to prevent any further internal damage. This process left me with a noticeable dent in my skull that would take some time to heal. It's amazing what a few meters and some gravity can do. After the surgery, I was unconscious for a pretty long while. My parents were told that my chances of survival were about 50% and that if I did pull through, it was likely I would be left with some permanent brain damage.

I don't remember much from my time at the hospital. They pumped me so full of painkillers that it became a blur. My parents have told me that I was there for a week or so, but even they have trouble remembering exactly; it was a traumatic time for all and I wasn't the only one who experienced the blur. I would wake up calling out for my brother in the night, they tell me, my eyes so swollen that I couldn't even tell what time it was. I was unrecognizable. A broken child in the dark of intermittent blindness.

When I was finally discharged to finish my recovery back at home, my life didn't just return to normal. Far from it. For weeks and weeks, I had to wear a neck brace and a special helmet while my skull healed. The helmet only came off to sleep. I looked like a race-car driver or an astronaut, but there was nothing fast or interstellar about my life during that time. The bruising took its sweet time to fade, and with it, a part of me faded as well. I was a changed boy. Gone was the extrovert: the active, jovial me. In his place, the introvert: a quieter self, a different model. It was like the real me had been swapped out when I was floating in that black infinity after impact. I'd been replaced, or possessed, or repurposed. I was me, but not me at all.

I fell three stories to the ground that year, when I was nine years old, but in many ways, I fell much, much farther. I fell into the beginnings of an abyss even greater than that black infinity I'd experienced. This was a defining moment for me. It changed the course of my life. After many more weeks, the swelling subsided and you could no longer see that I had been through something so arduous. With newly opened eyes, I began to see the world differently. I probably didn't know it then. Kids are aware of things we adults rarely are, but I don't think I possessed the self-awareness to see how important and pivotal this tragic situation would prove to be. Looking back now, it's so obvious in hindsight. *It was an awakening.*

I don't know if it was the trauma of a near-death experience. Maybe it was just the lingering effects of broken bones, surgeries, and painful healing. Whatever it was though, it was clear to me even then, at so young an age, that something was missing. Maybe even something that only the fall could help me see. All of a sudden, I knew there was a purpose for me— but there was a thick fog ahead, obscuring that purpose. The first year after my accident, this fog didn't let up much. It took me a while to see it, but there in the haze, there was a light. A lantern in the mist. Like something was beckoning me, summoning me. And when it finally emerged, there he was: my brother, ready to lead me, to show me something new. He had been trying on and off I suppose. I just wasn't picking up on it during my healing process. But his efforts became clear during these early days of awakening: He persuaded me to take my spirituality more seriously.

I wasn't sure I was up to the task, but he took me through it step by step. I started going to church. I found new comfort in the process of prayer. My family had never really gone to church. It was my brother who brought me into the fold, who taught me to use spirituality to shape myself and my aspirations. It became a form of therapy. There was an *energy* at work within this new community that surrounded me. I could feel it charging my being, charging my soul. It was within me.

Over the next few years, through my early teens, this source of guidance and energy was extremely valuable to me, in ways I'd never imagined possible. I began to hear a leading voice in my head. A distant echo pulling me toward something unknown. It was a serious turning point, but even this sense of direction couldn't solve everything completely. My introversion made me an easy target for bullies during my middle school days. And boy, did they come swinging—figuratively and literally. I ducked and weaved my way through those years, tolerating their nonsense as calmly as I could, trying my best to avoid conflict and deflect their negative energies. It was also during this time that I developed a deeper love of music. There was a piano in one of my classrooms that I would fool around with during recess or after school while the other kids played. I asked my parents to sign me up for lessons. The consequences of this addition to my life were exponential. Music became an instant outlet for me, for when I didn't speak much. This passion translated through my experience in church, and I began playing there as well. I believe this musicality helped bring my voice back; it helped me to be more extroverted, and to share with others. And it was also a form of energy in itself. After all, Instrumentation is just frequencies converging to form sounds. Today, I can look back on this time as the genesis of my understanding of energy and its various forms. It would inform my decisions for years to come. I had no idea how much so, but then, I was still traversing that fog that hung over me. I wasn't yet tuned in to the universe.

By the time I got to high school, the beginnings of this newfound voice had had enough of my bullies. My calm toleration had finally run out. My spirituality and musicality had been charging my soul like a battery, and it was time to use these energy reserves to my advantage. I started to stand up for myself more, to be more assertive and dominant in my everyday interactions. There were a few fights here and there. Nothing too serious, but enough to make me realize the power of confidence and self-esteem. Enough to make me realize that our reaction to action must be balanced—strong but measured. Yin and yang. My brother's mentorship through all of this was important. My prayers became more meaningful, more purposeful.

This developing sense of self-worth and self-actualization transitioned to my earliest experiences in meditation. I started reading books about it, and the deeper into the meditative process I went, the more that distant echo became clearer. The leading voice in my head provided me with both answers and directions. This was transformative. I was learning to channel my intentions, to sculpt my desires.

With high school behind me, I got a full scholarship to study engineering at university. I took up a few odd jobs on the side. Things went okay for a little while. I made some new friends, but nobody all that close. My brother had moved across the country for work, and with him gone, I left some good habits behind. I stopped meditating as often as I had been. During this time, I started to feel a little lost. My university experience wasn't fulfilling me as I thought it would, and the jobs I was taking on felt like dead ends. I hated feeling lost again, like I had when I was younger. I wondered how this reversal of confidence could happen; I had worked so hard to build new habits and take control of my life. My accident had taught me that there was a purpose for me, but I still hadn't figured out what it was. I grew easily bothered and stressed. My attitude deteriorated a little, and before long, through quick temper and easy frustration, I found myself in an actual physical altercation because of my poor judgment. Who was I becoming? A fight? Really? It was stupid. And kind of embarrassing. Even more embarrassing because I lost the fight. I lost a little dignity along with it. But this was a lightbulb moment for me.

It was the wake-up call I needed to come to terms with how I had been feeling. What I needed was more structure—and there was a way I could find that, while also making sure that if I ever got in a fight again, I'd be in a better position to win. I got into martial arts.

This was another powerful transition point for me. Martial arts led me to the practice of Tai Chi and Qigong. Increased strength and stamina soon followed as I renewed my spiritual focus and better aligned my life in equilibrium. For the most part, my practice of Qigong was self-taught, but I was fortunate to have an uncle whose mother had practiced with Shaolin monks many decades in the past. This allowed me to sharpen my skills a little faster than some, but believe me when I tell you: it's not the speed with which you make important changes that matters most. It's the intention and follow-through. The intensity of this meditation brought me more in touch with what was occurring inside my body. It made me realize that everything happening externally in my life was intricately connected with my inner balance. This was perhaps the first time that I began to understand the forces of energy in a concrete way—as a matter of mechanics. I started to come to terms with its flow, its transmission, and its infinite abilities. This was a learning process that would come in handy years later. Through Qigong, my meditations became so profound that I could literally feel the energy in my own body moving from one place to another, and I could direct it as needed. It was tangible. It was like a heat sensation coursing through my veins. What a feeling! I never wanted it to end!

My life started to turn around again after this. I got a better job at a law firm. I was starting to make a little bit of money for the first time. And I met a girl I was crazy about. Having someone close was great. Someone I could talk to about anything. I started reading a lot again, mostly about financial literacy and leadership. I wanted to build something of myself. I was determined to use the energy I could feel inside of me as a tool, to harness it for my own growth. I started reading about real estate investment. Something clicked. It was practically instantaneous. I knew what I had to do. I quit my job and leapt into the world of real estate. And you know what? I was pretty good at it! Things were finally falling into place again. And they kept getting better. It was the first time in my life when my happiness felt in balance with every aspect of my being. I felt so in control of my destiny. I still hadn't truly found that missing sense of purpose I was after, but it felt like I was on the right path. I had momentum.

Sometimes our paths are meant to bend and wind though... They can't always be straight lines. Things were really starting to take off for me. I started to feel as though maybe real estate investment was my purpose— maybe it was what I had been looking for. It was bringing me the freedom and flexibility I wanted, and it was creating a comfortable life for me and my fiancée, but it's easy to fly too close to the sun. As my work in this field expanded, so too did my aspirations of building an even bigger life for myself. I was still in search of *more* fulfillment, a *clearer* direction.

Soon after, I developed a working relationship with someone in the manufacturing field. It was a little outside my wheelhouse, but he took me under his wing, and the field seemed promising. He quickly became like a mentor to me. I bit off more than I could chew with this relationship though. And wow, did I learn that the hard way. As it turned out, my mentor wasn't who he said he was. He had been taking advantage of my eagerness and inexperience all along, enticing me with new opportunities and experiences. He did this by doing what so many scammers do, especially the online guru types: he was flashy and showy. Expensive watches, cars, homes, and other possessions that seemed too good to be true. He talked big and made even bigger promises. It was endless. He made me believe I could have it all, and after playing the long game, he wanted me to invest in his company, to become more of a partner. How could I say no? He had opened so many doors for me. It really did seem like he wanted to help me become a better version of myself. I thought of him as a mentor, and also as a friend. But none of it was real. Fake documents. Fake figures. Fake everything. It was all an illusion. He took me for everything. And I mean every penny! I'd taken out loans from family and friends and banks! I over-leveraged and over-extended to buy into a fake dream. I was financially ruined.

I never saw it coming. He had been grooming me to take a fall—a fall much greater than that day on the schoolyard when I was nine years old. Forget the three-storey tumble. I felt like he'd taken me to the top of a hundred-storey building. It was a bullet-fast elevator to the top and all along, he built up my confidence, earned my trust, and convinced me I was on the edge of truly making it to where I wanted to be… But there on that rooftop of false pretenses, as he was promising me the world, he shoved me over the edge, laughing at how gullible I was. A total conman!

So there I was, falling all over again, and sure, this time it was figurative… Call it a fall from grace, I guess. There were no broken bones or skull fractures or neck braces. But the impact was just as powerful. And the healing would be just as intense. Instead of hitting the ground, I hit the hardest thing of all: reality. Rock bottom, in all its icy coldness and indifference. But underneath that, if you let yourself keep going, is another side. Another dimension. Another reality. One of your own choosing. One where the internal energies I spent all those years learning to control unlock doors you didn't even know existed. This would be my last fall. I promised myself that. And more than that, I promised myself I would never be like him. I would never be a conman. I made a vow that I would never pretend to be something I wasn't, to always be truthful in how I represented myself. It's a vow I take incredibly seriously.

I found myself back at square one. As you can imagine, I sunk into a deep depression. This lowness became desperate and hungry. It ate me alive. It was a monster, and I was defenseless. In my hopelessness and despair, I lost even more. I lost my girlfriend. In my depleted mental state, I found it hard to keep fighting to make things work between us and we drifted apart. I tried chasing after her initially, but it was no use. My depression only worsened. They say the moments that break you make you stronger. It sure didn't feel like it at the time, but if you fall far enough and land hard enough, you're left just sitting there, looking around at all your broken pieces. I had been there before. I knew what had to be done.

I moved back to Vancouver and returned to the habits that had built me up before. I started practicing martial arts again and threw myself head-first into deeper and deeper meditation. During this time, I started working on new business strategies, schemes that eventually failed to pan out, but in working on proposals and plans, I tuned my focus. I had to. It was the only way to move forward. I started asking myself serious, introspective questions: *What kind of people did I want to work with? What kind of value did I want to provide to people? What type of work could help me deliver on truth, honesty, and transformation?* I knew that none of the ideas I was coming up with for my next chapter in life would allow me to answer these questions meaningfully—they were all just about making money. I wanted to do more than make money though. I wanted to benefit people deeply and spiritually! It took being taken advantage of and losing the first real love of my life for me to realize that I had to follow my passions, not my bank balance. I know that sounds cheesy, but clichés exist because they ultimately ring true.

One day while meditating, I found that powerful energy flow again at long last... The energy that I could literally feel pulsing from one part of my body to another. I had tapped into this level of meditation before, but it occurred to me that I had never really learned about what it was, or how it occurred. This was an aha moment—the kind Oprah always talks about. Something clicked in me. If I could share the fundamentals of this experience with people, maybe there was a business to build around it: a merging of science and spirituality. *Spiritual science.* I started researching soon after, but the bills still needed to be paid, so I pursued one of the business strategies I had been working on. I started a small online marketing company. It did okay, and I was able to get by while I plunged deep into every book and spiritual text I could get my hands on, digging deeper into the most profound effects of meditation.

One of the patterns I started to notice in my research was the various understandings of energy within the human body that each of the great ancient civilizations promoted. The Egyptians, Mesopotamians, Mayans, Aztecs, and more… all left behind records of targeted energy practices, especially sound energy and harmonics, or as we know it more commonly: frequency. This opened a rabbit hole. I was like Alice in Wonderland. I went all in, no looking back. I began studying the frequencies of the cosmos, of the planets themselves. This led me to uncover forms of meditation that relied upon these sorts of frequencies. In performing these meditations myself, I was amazed to experience how they affected my body and my emotions. It was incredible. The more I learned, and the more I put what I learned into practice personally, the more I understood the energy fields around my own body. This allowed me to take control of those fields, to adjust them, and in so doing, I was able to achieve a state of clarity I didn't even know existed. It was like all the blockages in my psyche and personality were cleared. My depression eased, my overall mood improved dramatically, and I could get into desired emotional zones almost on demand. If I needed to be focussed, I could tap into that energy. If I needed to be motivated, I could put myself in that mindset. Energy can be controlled. And the kind of energy you need can be manifested.

This all tied in with my prior experience with Qigong and its principles of energy flow. I began to experiment with new methods of meditation by incorporating those principles with my newfound scientific and historical understanding of frequencies and the ways they shape our physical and spiritual selves. I also started seeking out masters of energy control in the modern world, not just in the pages of history. I found Wim Hof and his amazing feats of body temperature manipulation (to combat extreme cold exposure) mind-blowing, so I merged his breathing techniques into my meditation routine. I also infused my practices with Kundalini. My online marketing company started to reach new heights as I tuned in to myself, and in my meditation, I prayed for a new place to channel the love and vibrance I was feeling inside. It was around this time that the woman who would become my wife emerged from the haze, almost like my brother had so many years before: A lantern in the dark. A compass to new prosperity. All of this renewed success and happiness was great, but it still wasn't sustaining me the way I knew my work and life needed to if I was to be truly fulfilled.

I knew my personalized practice of meditation was something special. I was manifesting the things I wanted in life. But achieving such an elevated state of consciousness through meditation isn't exactly duplicable. It can't really be packaged. Almost nobody has the time to put in the practice and effort required to achieve it. There had to be a way to tap into these levels of spiritual connection between mind, body, and spirit—and to gain the real-world results of drive, motivation, and manifestation, all of which can lead to abundance, success, and the control of one's destiny. I asked myself what lay at the heart of my personal meditation practice. What was it that made this inner harmony possible? It was the energy, the frequency. So what if frequencies could be crafted to elicit the changes in mind, body, and spirit that I was experiencing? There have been frequency therapy systems on the market for decades, but they've never truly been targeted before. I reached out to some scientists in related fields and we began developing frequencies, particularly higher quantum frequencies. This was it, I thought. This was how I could share my passions and build a business around them—a business that would help transform people's lives. We called this venture Qi Life.

Our goal was to create the ultimate frequency therapy system, a collection of frequencies, devices, and resources that would not only upset an industry that was stuck many decades in the past, but that would redefine how people use and engage with frequency in their everyday lives – making it modern, accessible, and easy to use. This was no simple task, and one that a lot of people were skeptical about in those early days, including me, if I'm being honest. I knew that there were many older technologies that people had claimed to have had some success with, but I was hoping to take things further.

One of the first trials I put to the test was on myself. Up until that point, I had suffered from a digestive disease that the medical community views as manageable but incurable. I'd tried everything. Pharmaceutical medication. Natural medication. Some worked okay, but their effects would wear off after my body got used to them so I was always having to switch them up and modulate my dosages. Acupuncture works for some, but I never really saw much in the way of results, and it was costly and inconvenient. My prayer and meditation allowed me to train my mind to tolerate the symptoms, even to forget about them at times, but while this was valuable, what I wanted most was a more permanent solution. Working with my team, we began testing frequencies on myself. It took some time to narrow down what worked best, but eventually, I started to see results. My symptoms diminished, and eventually, disappeared. The encouragement this self-healing journey brought me was euphoric. What else could we do with this technology?

My parents were some of the first users. My father had spent years suffering from the effects of chronic insomnia. He was lucky to sleep more than an hour or two per night. It drained him physically and emotionally. After experimenting with various frequencies, we finally found one that helped him see some early results. We kept fine-tuning, and before long, he was sleeping almost the whole night. It's been many years since then, and he's still experiencing a good night's rest. My mom was also an early adopter. When she had a stroke, I used frequency therapy to help her through her recovery. She was able to get back to normal living much sooner than expected, and notably faster than the other stroke patients in her hospital ward. Her doctors were amazed by her rapid progression. As I transitioned beyond family and friends, the results kept coming in positive. I was gaining confidence in the consistency of this technology's effectiveness. The last of my doubts and skepticism began to disappear. People were using our frequencies to improve their focus and clarity, to promote better sleep habits, to induce ultra-relaxation and achieve profound states of meditation. They reported better mood fluctuation and relief from anxieties, stress, and pain. I felt like I was witnessing miracles daily. As the devices and technology improved, the testimonials I was hearing made it clear I had chosen the right path, that I was truly doing something meaningful.

I remember the wife I spoke with from Hong Kong. Her husband had been dealing with forty years of back pain. A sporting incident pushed this pain to its breaking point. He fractured his spine, and the surgery he received only made it worse, leaving him in severe pain. He barely left the house. She bought one of our devices and began targeting specific frequencies to his back once a day. After just two months, he was walking again! She told me about how it had also affected his mood and personality. He was happier and had more energy. He even started cooking again, something he hadn't done in years.

I remember hearing from a man in Indiana. His brother had to have one of his feet amputated and spent most of his time bedridden. He had painful varicose up to his knees: swelling, discomfort, and discolouration. With daily application of frequency therapy, the varicose all but disappeared in less than a week. It even reduced the size of an ulcer he had on his remaining foot, clearing it up soon after!

I remember my friend Will, a music producer from Canada. He was active and healthy. He practiced martial arts and had great self-discipline, but something was still missing. He felt like he wasn't living up to his potential. Using our Qi Coil™ device and frequencies designed for manifestation and abundance, he experienced increased focus and creativity. His business grew and new opportunities started to present themselves—things he never would have dreamed about before.

The power of these transformations never got old to me, and it still doesn't. And as Qi Life continued to grow, I knew I had to keep pushing to bring this technology to as many people as I could share it with.

The longer I work in this field, the more I've come to realize how incredibly life-changing this technology is. I'm not just a developer or inventor... I'm a user. I'm a believer. I've seen the evidence firsthand. These products have changed my life. They've allowed me to finally find that piece of me that was missing, that sense of purpose. I get to wake up every day combining my passions and talents in order to help other people find their inner balance and self-healing pathways—all without pills, without surgeries, without invasive treatments.

Modern healthcare is reactive. It reacts to the shortcomings in our mind, body, and spirit. It's at its best in emergencies or last resort situations, like when I fell three storeys as a child, but it's not so good at maintenance and preventative healing. Ancient civilizations knew better. Modern monks high in the Himalayas still know better to this day. The answer is to be anticipatory and responsive, not reactive. The secret to overall balance is energy flow. It's the fields of subtle energy within us and around us. Being able to modulate these fields and control them... That's the secret to strengthening ourselves from the inside so we can manifest our desires on the outside, so we can awaken ourselves spiritually. It's the secret to achieving true happiness.

I still feel those old sensations of isolation, depression, or anxiety from time to time, but what I've learned is that with the right skills, methods, and technology, I can literally flip the switch on those feelings, and ultimately overcome them instead of languishing in them. Happiness is being able to do what you want and be the person you're meant to be, to pursue your bigger dreams with fewer roadblocks and less resistance. Today, through my work, I get to help people just like you find that same sense of personal control. You *can* be abundant. You *can* be successful. You *can* be at peace. You *can* be healthy. You *can* be in balance. Resonant frequency is your passport to a whole new self.

Looking forward, my vision for Qi Life is to work with an even broader range of people and holistic practitioners so they can develop their own businesses with the technology we create. We're increasing funding in our research and development to be at the forefront of innovation in this space, and are carrying out clinical trials to substantiate our work even further so it can reach even more people. Our product line will continue to expand to meet more specific needs, and we're working on educational products and resources so these innovations can be better understood and more easily accessible. Our ultimate goal has always been to build a robust community of people who are capable of supporting each other. This is the Qi Life mission, and you're invited to take part.

My life has been a series of valleys and peaks. I've known the most desperate lows. I've fallen, literally and figuratively, enough times to know that aligning your inner-self with the world around you is hard. It can be painful. It can seem hopeless. But that alignment is critical. Balancing your energies and targeting them in the same direction as your ambitions and aspirations is the greatest pathway to personal achievement in every aspect of your life. You deserve your balance. I believe you *can* change yourself 1% a day. It's the steadfast determination to improve the little pieces of your life with the intention to improve the whole.

Manifestation.
Attraction.
Abundance.
Harmony.
Happiness.
Success.
TOTAL. ENERGY. TRANSFORMATION.
Unlock your inner potential. Change your life.

I've made it my life's mission to help others, like you, find their own awakening… no treacherous falls required. It's a long way down still, but it's a descent into your own inner workings, deep into your sense of self. It's a journey that leads back to the top. I want to help you along that journey.

That's why I've compiled this book. I want to share with you one of the most empowering secrets the universe has to offer: energy. Qi. It's a secret that can change your life. One that has extensive scientific backing. In each section of this book, I will outline the powers of this energy form that you never knew existed—the ones you can take control of yourself. I'll discuss how this energy can be used to heal, and how physics proves it's possible. I'll go into what's next, and how our understanding of science will open new frontiers of possibility for personal transformation. I'll explore superhuman abilities, and how amazing feats are happening all around us. I'll talk about the multiverse, how manifestation is real and yours to explore. And I'll share with you what we've been developing at Qi Life, and how our technologies can become your secret weapons of choice in your quest for reinvention.

If you've picked up this book, it means you already have the inner desire required to transform yourself. Desire and reality are on the same wavelength. The distance between them can be measured in energy. Luckily for us, the universe speaks in energy. It can be a little subtle sometimes, but its healing properties are out of this world. You just need to know how to translate them, embrace them… to live *your* Qi life.

Want to kickstart your own Qi Awakening? Why not start today? Start seeing the world with fresh new eyes. Spiritual *attunement* will produce the state of consciousness you've been looking for.

- Activate your third eye and pineal gland
- Increase your creativity
- Enhance your intuition, insight, and imagination
- Encourage more vivid dreams, and improve dream recall
- Experience *your* spiritual awakening
- Increase your bio-energy
- Improve stress and anxiety

Download my Spiritual Awakening Third Eye higher quantum frequency absolutely **free.** It's the perfect gateway to the technologies my team and I have developed. See and feel the results for yourself—my gift to you.

>>> **Visit www.UseTheQi.com to download your free meditation frequency.**

CHAPTER 2
ENERGY HEALING

WHAT IS QI?

For most people, the concept of Qi is rooted in a simple understanding of energy flow and its general benefits for well-being and balance. I covered the core principles of this subtle energy form earlier in the introduction, but let's take another look at the basics so we can move forward with a strong grasp of the concept.

Qi is the essence of life and consciousness. It responds to both internal and external factors. It fluctuates constantly, and flows through all matter, both living and inanimate. It has two polarities, yin and yang, which must flow in harmony for good health to be maintained. In its most simplistic translation, Qi means 'vapors' or 'breath'. In this sense, the ancient Chinese considered it to be as critical to our health as air itself. (Swanson, 2010) But this definition is quite basic and lacks a more subtle nuance. If you were to flip through the pages of an extended Chinese dictionary, you would find upwards of 85 unique definitions, plus many more that only make sense as part of compound phrases or expressions. Take the term *hao qi*, which means generous spirit or *hao ran zhi qi*, which means elevation of mind. If we view Qi as an essential building block of the universe, then we can better understand the phrase *yuan qi*, which translates as 'primary matter'. As you can see, this tiny word holds enormous meaning and power. (Dong; Raffill, 2006)

In the Chinese tradition, *yuan qi* is imbued at birth. This primary matter is interconnected with *tian qi, di qi,* and *ying qi* (heaven Qi, earth Qi, and nourishment Qi) to form *zhen qi*: true Qi. True Qi moves within our bodies to affect our every action, and because it is a product of its contributing types of Qi, it forms the union of man and the natural world, and by extension, the universe as a whole. This explains how Qi can be transferred or projected, with or without physical contact—because it is primary matter. It exists in everything. It *is* everything. (Dong; Raffill, 2006)

The Chinese were not alone in recognizing this powerful energy force. Ancient Indians referred to it as 'prana'. Australian aboriginals referred to it as 'songlines'. (Devereux, 1999, 2003) The Iroquois of Canada called it 'orendo'. It was 'mana' to the Polynesian peoples. North African tribes referred to it as 'bareka'. The ancient Greeks called it 'pneuma'—which translates to 'that which is breathed'. (Devereux, 1999; Michell, 1969) In virtually every interpretation of this energy, no matter the culture or civilization, its foundation as being as important as the air in our lungs has been central, and it is for this reason that the manipulation and control of this energy, in order to balance it consciously, has almost always been centered around breathing techniques during meditative practices.

This ancient wisdom teaches that energy permeates everything and links all beings with their surroundings. Developing knowledge of and control over the flow of this energy provides for stability and longevity of mind, body, and spirit. Chinese Confucian philosopher Mencius described Qi as well-integrated within the body. He proposed that when

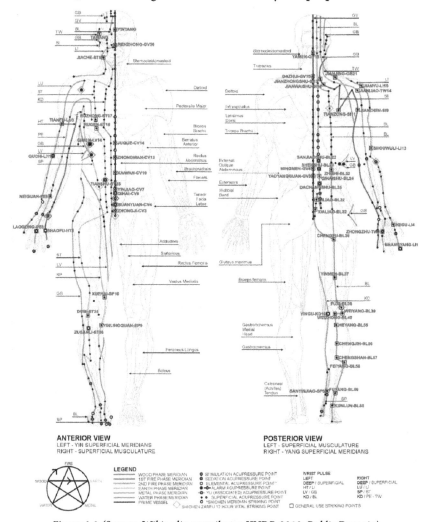

Figure 1.1 *(Source: Wikipedia contributor KVDP, 2010, Public Domain)*
The body's meridian system.

properly tended to, Qi was powerful enough to flow beyond the body and its immediate surroundings—that it could reach and connect with the universe itself. (Lau, 2003) In this sense, Qi is also present in non-living entities, because it is the basic building block of the cosmos. Philosopher Zhuangzi wrote that Qi accumulates to create the material world, and dissipates when matter breaks down and returns to the universe. (Watson, 2013) A balance of Qi, therefore, is a balance of existence. To balance this energy within ourselves is to balance our existence within the universe. Energy in harmony.

Western doctors and scientists have expressed skepticism about this subtle energy form from the earliest encounters between West and East. As early as the 1840s, German scientists tried to evaluate the powers of Qi, but hesitancy and disbelief broke down any real efforts to research this energy in depth. This hesitancy has caused great delays in making ground-breaking improvements in medicine and therapy available to all. More modern attempts have started to chip away at this hesitancy, finally. In studying the practice of acupuncture, South Korean scientists have identified tiny channels in our bodies that energy flows through. These channels have long been recognized by ancient civilizations, and have been referred to as 'meridians' or 'lines' through which Qi circulates in the body. (Yu, 2002) Eastern European physicists have amassed a growing body of work that suggests that this energy circulation obeys the laws of physics in ways that our current understandings can't yet account for. (Swanson, 2010)

For ancient cultures, it was accepted that Qi came in many forms. An origin variant is inherited at birth, while subsequent forms are accumulated or manifested during life through experi- ence, choices, and actions. This accumulation results in a Qi field, or energy field, that surrounds beings and objects, and these fields constantly interact positively or negatively with one another. We have the individual power to manipulate our own Qi fields through practice, meditation, and the use of tools, and by extension, we also have the power to project our Qi energy onto other beings or entities. (Gu, 2009, 2011; Hin, 2010) This power of controlling, cultivating, manipulating, and projecting Qi is a practice known as 'Qigong'.

WHAT IS QIGONG?

Mentions of Qigong, or rather, descriptions of its practice, date back as far as mentions of Qi itself in written records and artwork—more than 3,000 years. In some cases, archeological finds date the practice to as old or older than 5,000 years, such as the Neolithic pottery seen here, which appears to show a figure in a Qigong position. From the breathing techniques described during the Zhou Dynasty, to the specific instructions on how to concentrate the movement of Qi found inscribed on precious jewels around 600 BC, history is clear: Qigong forms a substan- tial and time-cherished set of practices and traditions. In the 500s AD, during the Liang Dynasty, records show that Qi masters began to understand the effects of Qigong on overall health, strength, and stamina. (Swanson, 2010)

Figure 1.2 *(Source: licenses unknown)* Neolithic pottery depicting the practice of Qigong, specifically the posture technique known as 'standing post'.

Qigong translates to 'life energy cultivation'. Put simply, it is the use of breathing, movement, and meditation (Cohen, 2009) to enable a Qi balance. But more than that, in traditional Chinese medicine, Qigong is also used to enable preventative and curative outcomes. (Holland, 2000) In other words, it is a form of energy healing, not just for the body, but for the mind and spirit as well. Daoism, Buddhism, and Confucianism have all promoted Qigong as a means to achieve higher consciousness, physical longevity, self-defense, and enhanced moral character. (Cohen, 1999; Liang, 1997; Yang, 1998) You can see then that Qigong, or energy healing, is a holistic approach to ailments, deficiencies, and shortcomings of all kinds, and can be implemented in many ways to target specific aspects of one's life.

More than seventy-five forms of Qigong practice can be found in literature through the millennia (Ma Ji Ren, 1992), but most fall into five predominant varieties or categories, each of which focuses on different intentions of energy flow. Daoist Qigong maintains the physical body and higher spiritual cultivation. Confucianist Qigong focuses on moral character and acumen. Martial Qigong develops self-defense and the control of physicality. Buddhist Qigong liberates the mind and nourishes life. And medical Qigong heals the self and others. (Swanson, 2010)

In terms of general procedure, Qigong is carried out through dynamic practice, static practice, meditative practice, and external practice (which uses external agents). Dynamic practice involves fluid, choreographed body movement, with an emphasis on breath control and spatial awareness. (Frantzis, 2008) Static practice involves holding various postures for prolonged periods of time, similar to the practice of yoga. (Diepersloot, 2000) Meditative practice involves visualization, sound, breath awareness, and a focus on channeling Qi circulation—all with a purpose and intention to still the mind and seek enlightenment.

(Lu, 1969) And finally, external practice, which involves the use of the world around us. This could include special herbs, drinks, and foods which are ingested to affect one's Qi. It could also be through physical touch, massage, or interaction with other beings. It could take the form of specialized devices which manipulate Qi energy flow both within and outside the body. And it may also include the external and outward projection of Qi away from the body, targeted at another being or entity, either at close range or from a distance. (Liang, 1997; Xu, 2000)

The term 'Qigong' itself came into use in the 1940s and 1950s when the Chinese government started to incorporate the many forms of this practice into one cohesive system of life-preserving practices and philosophical traditions. (Voigt, 2013) In the years that followed, through the Great Leap Forward and the Cultural Revolution, this streamlined Qigong was implemented in rehabilitation centers, hospitals, and university science departments across China. This led to a renewed scientific interest in the benefits and outcomes that Qigong has to offer. Today, it is estimated that more than 200 million people practice some form of Qigong daily within China's borders, with tens of millions more joining in around the world. From its simple benefits like daily calm and clarity, to its more intensive outcomes like healing and preventative medicine, to its most incredible achievements in mastery like curative and survivalist feats, Qigong represents a far-reaching and all-encompassing set of tools that challenge our understanding of physics, biology, and the universe itself. It's no wonder so many civilizations and cultures came to the same conclusions: Qi is our foundational energy source, and its mastery can take humanity to new levels of consciousness and well-being.

MASTERY AND HEALING FEATS

In the introduction to this book, we took a glimpse at the astounding, long-distance energy projection of Qigong master Jixing Li. From more than 3,000 miles away, he was able to transmit his healing energy to eradicate sample cancer cells stored in incubators. His projection was so precise that he could even target his energy to a single shelf in a specific room. From California to Pennsylvania, Master Li's experiments under Penn State University's Professor John Neely documented both the precision and efficacy of projected subtle energy, or Qi.

Across China, India, and other places where civilizations date back thousands of years, Master Li's abilities would not seem so far-fetched as they may in the newer nations and cultures of the West. It is this unwillingness to accept alternative practices that have kept us from advancing in the modern world. What we refer to as 'paranormal' is simply *normal* in other places.

Paul Dong has written extensively on paranormally gifted energy practitioners across China. His work has showcased many examples of amazing individuals. (Dong, 1984, 1997) In his 1997 book *China's Super Psychics*, Dong describes Master Yan Xin, a medical doctor whose practice specialized in applying Qi energy on his patients. One of Yan's most famous patients was Deng Jiaxian, a leading nuclear scientist, whose advanced cancer had reached terminal status. Having exhausted all traditional forms of medicine and therapy, Dr. Yan was summoned to the hospital to see if he could help the dying scientist. On his travels to the hospital, Yan started his energy projection. By the time of his arrival, the scientist was sitting up in bed without the aid of painkillers. This lack of pain continued for the final month of Deng Jiaxian's life while Yan kept applying his Qi energy to the patient. The scientist ultimately passed away, but the fact that he required no anesthetics to cope with his failing body in these final weeks was seen as nothing short of a miracle.

Yan's energy healing has been extensively analyzed. One of his patients, a steel worker who was hit by a truck and suffered serious fractures in his shoulders, described Yan Xin's energy projection as a "cool and refreshing stream of energy." After just a few minutes of therapy with the master, the steelworker was not only able to lift a fifty-pound weight without issue, but X-rays also revealed his fractures had been reduced to mere hairlines.

Other documented patient cases include diabetes cures, tumor size reductions, and even reversing HIV-positivity. (Dong, 1997). In his world travels to lecture at various conferences and universities, Dr. Yan Xin is well known for his Qi emissions on his audience members, where many attendees have confirmed various pains and ailments being alleviated or eradicated on the spot.

Versions of this sort of energy-based healing extend deep into the pages of our human story. The ancient Greeks recorded many such instances. Take the story of King Pyrrhus, for example. He was said to be able to heal the afflictions of his poor subjects simply by touching them. The Egyptians spoke of an energy force sourced from the star system Sirius. They called it 'sekhem' and it was primarily practiced by the Egyptian priesthood. Practitioners would channel energy through their hands and into the patient. They could also do this without the physical touch, what we call today 'remote healing'. The Bible has dozens of examples of energy healing, many of which were performed by Jesus himself. From healing the blind, to healing lepers, Jesus' touch is said to be the flow of God's own energy into the person in need of healing.

The Japanese form of this phenomenon is known as 'reiki'. Japanese healers transferred what they referred to as 'universal energy' through their hands, particularly through their palms, in order to facilitate physical and emotional recovery. Perhaps there is no greater visual reference for this practice than in the famous film *Karate Kid*, in which Daniel is hurt during his big tournament fight, and his sensei, Mr. Miyagi practices Reiki to ease his pain so he can continue fighting. (Avildsen, 1984) Reiki finds its roots in the concepts of Qi. Its teachings describe Qi in a physiological context—energy that can be manipulated to treat illness and injury.

"When the flow of Qi is impaired, we have disease. When it flows easily, we have perfect health." These are the words of Master Hong Liu. (Liu, 1997) Hong Liu was an apprentice of Master Kwan, who was a famed Qigong practitioner known for living in a cave in the mountains outside of Canton, in Southern China, during the Cultural Revolution. (Congressional Record, 2012) Hong Liu recalls his experiences observing Master Kwan at work as nothing short of miraculous. "He never asked what ailment the patient had. Instead, he looked at the person briefly. [...] Then he would just blurt out the patient's illness and where it bothered the patient most." (Liu, 1997) Master Kwan was known for his ability to project Qi onto the body from his hands. His teachings dictated three means by which Qi could be transmitted to encourage healing:

1. by using acupuncture needles
2. by physical touch applied to acupuncture points
3. by long-distance projection (remote healing)

Master Hong Liu learned all of these methods diligently, and as he went through his formal Western medical training, he incorporated his Qigong studies into his laboratory research in an attempt to measure the effects of Qi energy application. In one study, which used traditional angiography techniques (adding a dye to the bloodstream to monitor blood flow), Hong Liu and his team discovered that Qi transmission for as little as thirty-seconds resulted in increased circulation. His later work with animals infected with cancer documented that 75% of the animals who were treated with Qigong saw dramatic reductions in tumor size. (Liu, 1997)

These miraculous phenomena are not just isolated to Chinese masters of subtle energy. A study carried out in Brazil examined the effects of energy transmission by Umbanda tribal masters. These masters were challenged with transmitting energy 6,000 miles away, all the way to Las Vegas, Nevada. The recipients of this remote exercise experienced an increase in fingertip blood volume, as well as increased electrodermal activity. (Radin, 2001c)

Elsewhere, we can examine the techniques of Guru Paramahansa

Yogananda of India. Born in the late 1800s, this yogi was known for popularizing the practice of Kriya Yoga, which emphasizes rhythmic hyperventilation at different rates of breathing during the meditation process, which was said to transform his followers' inner energy balance. In his 1946 autobiography, Yogananda explained the energy effects that this form of meditation had on the body as a "psycho-physiological method by which [...] the yogi transmutes his cells into pure energy. Elijah, Jesus, Kabir and other prophets were past masters in the use of Kriya or a similar technique, by which they caused their bodies to materialize and dematerialize at will." Many studies have been carried out on Yogananda's techniques in the decades since his death in 1952. One such study examined the effects of Kriya in the treatment of depression. It concluded that Kriya Yoga showed promise as an alternative treatment for people suffering from melancholic depression. (Janakiramaiah, 2000) Studies like this one confirm that the flow of energy, or Qi, is not just a matter of physical health, but also a matter of mental health.

Guru Yogananda falls into the category of Pranic healers. Much like Qi masters, Pranic healers have a focussed command over the subtle energy that flows through us. For the sake of distinction, allow me to outline the basic principles of Prana versus Qi. Like Qi, mentions of Prana

The 3 Major Nadis (rivers) **and the 7 Chakras** (wheels of energy)

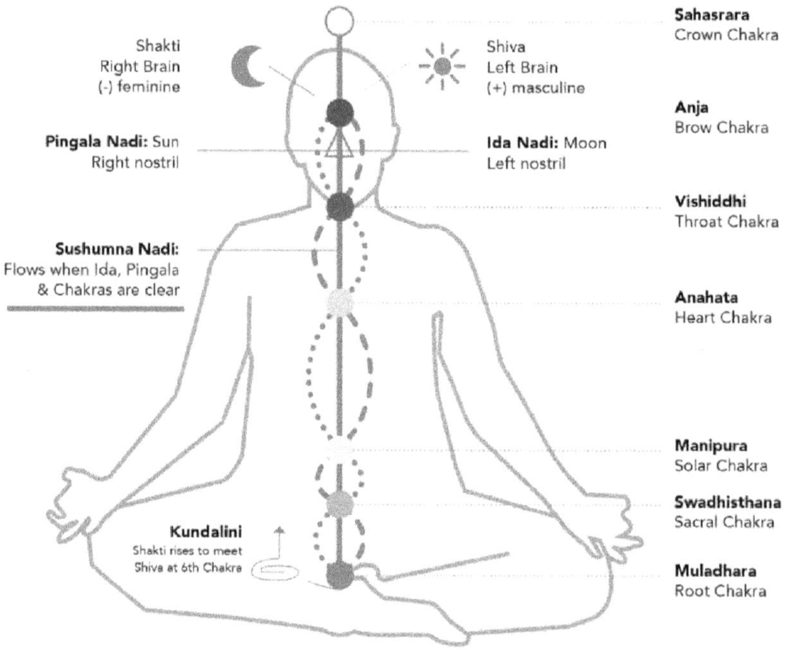

Figure 1.3 *(Source: TheModernVedic.com, license unknown)*
The major bodily nadis and chakras.

date back more than 3,000 years, and just like Qi, it translates to 'life force', or what Indian gurus called the 'vital principle'. This energy form is said to permeate reality on all levels, both in living beings and inanimate objects. It is believed to connect all the elements of the universe. (Saraswati, 1981)

Ancient Indian philosophy describes Prana flowing through channels within the body just as Qi does. (Mallinson, 2017) They call these channels 'nadis'. Fluctuations in the flow of Prana through the nadis are said to cause physical and mental agitation. (Sridhar, 2015) You can see then that the Indians and the Chinese both came to virtually the same conclusions about the special role that universal, cosmic energy plays, both within the body and without.

Tirumalai Krishnamacharya, sometimes referred to as the 'father of modern yoga', was a master of Pranic healing. The tales of his use of Prana to help heal or cure are legendary. He is said to have been able to stop his pulse, stop cars with his hands, and lift heavy objects with ease. (Pagés Ruiz, 2001) One of his more notable energy healing feats took place in the early 1900s. Invited to the Himalayas by Lord Irwin, the Viceroy of Simla, Krishnamacharya was asked to help Irwin with his diabetes. The guru spent six months teaching the Viceroy advanced yoga techniques. Lord Irwin's health improved so much that he funded Krishnamacharya's pilgrimage through Tibet to study with a master near Nepal. (Mohan, 2010) Krishnamacharya healed many people in his lifetime, focusing on a tailored approach for each patient, including himself. At the age of ninety-six, he suffered a hip fracture. For most people of this advanced age, a fracture of this kind would be a death sentence. Krishnamacharya refused surgery, opting to treat himself with a specialized course of Pranic healing that he could perform in his bed. His hip healed and he went on to live another four years, dying at the age of one-hundred. Krishnamacharya believed that energy was universal. A student of his recalls the mindset the guru encouraged when meditating: "Think of God. If not God, the sun. If not the sun, your parents." (Pagés Ruiz, 2001) Everything is connected. Energy is the building block, but it is also the tool to build beyond.

This building block, although subtle, is uniquely powerful when harnessed. You'll remember how Master Jixing Lee worked with Penn State University to transmit energy from California to Pennsylvania. This sort of research is becoming the standard, promising amazing new opportunities for traditional medicine to be supplemented or replaced by energy healing techniques. Another study of this kind involved a type of energy transmission developed by Master Choa Kok Sui, who was also a scientist and chemical engineer. The research was carried out at the University of California Irvine and revolved around the use of energy on cells contained in petri dishes. The cells were subjected to lethal doses of gamma radiation. Using energy transmission, Dr. Joie Jones set out to examine whether healing energy could slow, reverse, or even stop the radioactivity from completely killing the cells. (Jones, 2008) Typically, after a radioactive dosage, most cells experience a 50% die-off rate after twenty-four hours. The cells that had healing energy applied to them saw their survival rate jump up to 88%. This amazing success rate occurred regardless of whether the energy practitioner was nearby or transmitting from long-distance! These results weren't isolated either. Five-hundred-and-twenty experiments were conducted with ten different Pranic healers and Qigong masters. (Jones, 2006)

SCIENCE BEHIND THE MASTERY

I've laid out the concepts of Qi, its practice through Qigong, and how some of its foremost masters have utilized their understanding of subtle energy, and how to control it, to carry out amazing feats of energy healing. But what differentiates these masters from casual practitioners? What is it about a strong command of Qi that gives them these abilities? Qigong is very often a form of psychokinesis: the ability to influence a physical system (the material world, both living and inanimate) without physical interaction. (Xiong, 2010). As we've covered, it is the transmission of energy from one entity to another.

But what is energy? In simple terms, energy is just frequency: waves of invisible force traveling through space and time. We are constantly affected by frequencies of all kinds. From the devices we use, to the sun's rays, from inside our bodies at the cellular level, and even from the Earth itself. Some frequencies are bad for us. Others are good.

It was famed German physicist, Winfried Otto Schumann, who discovered that the Earth itself generates a resonant frequency: 7.83hz. (Montiel, 2005) This was a remarkable discovery because it is around this frequency that our brains' alpha waves resonate. (Foster, 2017) Basically, this frequency acts as a background energy field that affects our biological circuitry. (Dispenza, 2019) Frequencies influence everything from our immune systems to our general cognitive well-being. Research has shown that deep meditation, like subtle energy masters practice, increases our alpha wave power. (Lomas, 2015)

In 1964, German scientist Rütger Wever began experimenting with how energy affects our bodies. He and his team had an underground bunker constructed where volunteers could reside for various periods of time, unaffected by the frequency energy that that exists on the Earth's surface. In the absence of this energy, Wever's test subjects began feeling ill, experienced headaches, and their sleep cycles were thrown off. To see what would happen if above-ground conditions were replicated in the bunker, Wever and his team introduced energy fields without telling the test subjects. With generators emitting the 7.83hz frequency, the volunteers experienced immediate response. Their anxiety, headaches, and emotional distress either disappeared or decreased. (Dispenza, 2019; Wirz-Justice, 2005) These studies forever linked the connection between human health and the natural frequency of the planet, otherwise known as the 'Schumann Resonance'. In essence, they proved something practitioners of energy healing have known for over 3,000 years: that energy is everything.

Israeli-American scientist Itzak Bentov put it like this: he believed that illness and ill-being were nothing more than "out-of-tune behaviour" within the body. When part of the body is out-of-tune, he suggested its frequency has been altered, causing it to vibrate out of rhythm. By reintroducing a harmonizing rhythm, the proper tune could be reconfigured, returning balance and well-being. (Bentov, 1977)

If there's one thing modern science is very good at, it's energy measurement. And as you might expect, energy healers have been studied extensively from this perspective. Surely if these individuals possess the ability to control the energy within them, then that energy can be measured.

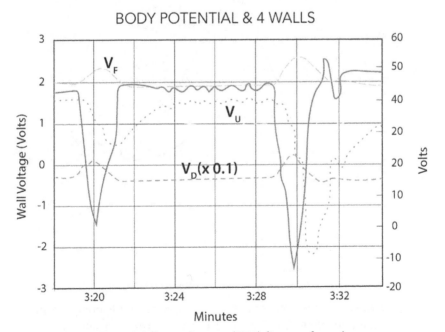

Figure 1.4 *(Source: Swanson (2003), license unknown)*
Dr. Green's voltage results with energy healers.

In 1993, Dr. Elmer Green of the Menninger Clinic designed a series of experiments to do just that. He constructed a special laboratory that could isolate a test subject from external energy fields. This would allow him to measure the subjects' energy outputs without outside energy pollution affecting the results. He intended to assess how much voltage or charge these individuals created from within their bodies. What he found was astounding; his test subjects were capable of generating sizable internal voltages and were able to project that charge several feet within the confines of his specialized laboratory. (Green, 1993; Tiller, 1997)

The energy healers tested demonstrated up to 10,000 times the normal voltage of a typical adult. Rather than the normal average of 0.010 to 0.015 volts, these healers registered between 30 and 300 volts! (Green, 1993) One test subject produced fifteen voltage pulses in just thirty minutes. Interestingly, these pulses generally originated from the naval region on their bodies. This is where Qigong masters are taught to collect and store their Qi energy reserves prior to transmitting it. This area of the body is known as the second chakra in Pranic healing and Tantric philosophy. (Swanson, 2003)

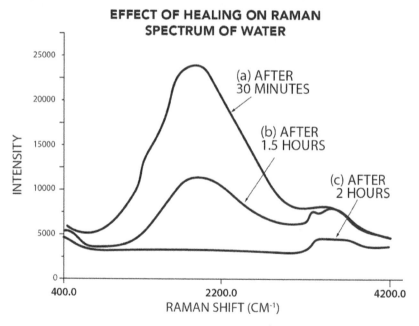

EFFECT OF HEALING ON RAMAN SPECTRUM OF WATER

Figure 1.5 *(Source: Swanson (2003), license unknown)*
Dr. Yan Xin's Raman spectroscopy results.

This research is not the only example of measurable energy control. In the 1980s and 1990s, Dr. Yan Xin, a Qigong master himself, conducted research on the effects of energy projection on water. Using a technique called Raman spectroscopy, the vibrational modes of molecules can be measured. When a sample substance, like water, is subjected to an external frequency, the spectroscopy measures the effect the frequency has on the substance's chemical bonds, essentially observing its molecular vibrational change, if any. (Gardiner, 1989) This change registers on the Raman spectrum. Dr. Yan's work showed that water targeted by Qi energy experienced higher peaks of vibrational change than typical ambient or background energy fields allow for. This cannot be explained by conventional science, and similar results have been replicated more than fifty times in the years since. (Swanson, 2010) When you consider that our bodies are composed of more than 65% water, it becomes quite obvious that Qi energy can have a great effect on our physical form.

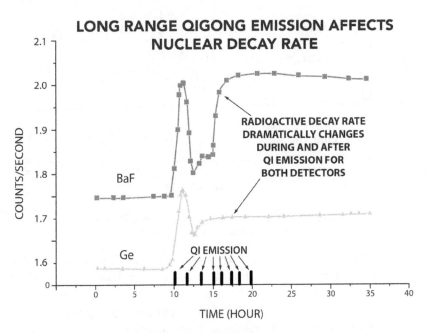

Figure 1.6 *(Source: Swanson (2003), license unknown)*
Dr. Yan Xin's radioactive decay results.

Curious to see what other substances could be affected by Qi projection, Yan carried out several experiments using radioactive material. The decay rate of radioactive material is considered to be a constant. By targeting radioactive samples with Qi energy, Yan was able to observe a slower or greater speed of decay virtually on request. He conducted these experiments at close range and at distances up to 2,000 kilometers away from the sample material. The results saw a 9.5% average increase in the speed of decay, and an 11.3% average decrease in decay rate depending on how the Qi energy was targeted. (Yan, 1988, 2000)

In reviewing Dr. Yan's experiments, Dr. Qian Xuesen, the chairman of the Chinese Association of Science and Technology, concluded that this research "unequivocally demonstrates that without touching substances, the human body can affect them and change their molecular structures and properties." (Lu, 1997)

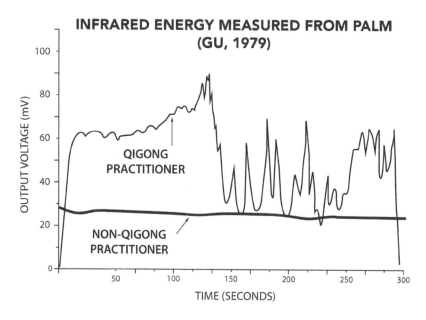

Figure 1.6 *(Source: Swanson (2003), license unknown)*
Dr. Gu Hansen's infrared results.

Another way to measure energy is by the heat it creates. This can be done through infrared output analysis. Dr. Gu Hansen, a physicist from the Shanghai Institute of Nuclear Physics, researched time-varying infrared radiation (IR) emitted from the hands of Qigong masters. The human body is constantly releasing heat radiation, but Gu suspected that energy masters likely released more than the average person. And he was right. His studies in the 1970s confirmed that the average person emits infrared radiation at a relatively constant output, with no notable pulsation. Qigong masters, however, emitted inconsistent IR output; the IR would pulse when the master emitted Qi energy. (Gu, 1978)

This research inspired Dr. Lu Zuyin to look into the magnetic field effect of energy masters. Magnetic field effect, or magnetic induction, is measured in a unit called gauss. Masters were observed to emit up to 25 gausses, which is fifty times stronger than the Earth's magnetic field! (Swanson, 2010) And there's something about electromagnetism that's worth special mention…

ELECTROMAGNETISM: ENERGY FIELDS AT WORK

Electromagnetism is key to the concepts of Qi and Qigong. Electromagnetic healing devices and therapies represent one of the few areas in mainstream Western medical research and healthcare where doctor and consumer acceptance of energy healing is the norm. Arguably the most prevalent examples of this are Rife machines and P.E.M.F. (Pulsed Electromagnetic Field) therapy technologies.

Dr. Royal Rife was a medical scientist and engineer whose work in the early 1900s introduced a radical shift in how illnesses could potentially be treated. His advanced optical compound microscopes changed the way organisms could be viewed at close range—17,000x magnification. Using these devices to research cures for tuberculosis, Rife noticed something peculiar: microscopic organisms had their own electrical polarities, oscillation patterns, and other electrical characteristics. (Dunn, 1931; New York Times, 1931) He wondered what might happen if he subjected these microscopic specimens to electrical frequencies. In so doing, Rife discovered he was able to 'devitalize' cells. In other words, his experiments demonstrated the slowing down or destruction of certain pathogens, bacteria, and viruses at the cellular level. With this knowledge and observation, and putting his electrical engineering background to use, Rife began developing specialized devices to target unique frequencies on specific organisms. (Jones, 1938)

Rife recalibrated his research to find the so-called 'cancer virus', which he believed was the secret to curing cancer. In 1932, he inadvertently stumbled upon a morphed cancer culture that had been sitting in a tube near one of his electromagnetic current devices. It had been left there for twenty-four hours by accident, but the results of its proximity to the device prompted him to repeat the experiment, this time on purpose. Over and over again—one-hundred-and-four times to be exact, he and his team uncovered an isolated, filtrable carcinoma virus, visible through his most advanced device to date, called the Universal Microscope. With such close observation, he was able to determine the frequency of the virus, allowing him to fine-tune his frequency-generating devices in order to target the cancer virus in isolation. (Lynes, 1987, 2017) At the time, cancer accounted for around 123,000 deaths per year and was beginning to increase steadily. (CDC [Murphy], 1935)

Over the next two years, he and his team worked with small animals like rats and guinea pigs, inoculating them with cancer, and then treating them with frequency generating devices. Experiment after experiment, they found that the cancers in the animals were reduced or eliminated, all without any notable harm caused to the creatures. Altogether, Rife carried out over four-hundred tests on his animal subjects. The results were overwhelming. They were successfully curing cancer. It was time to test his procedures on humans. (Lynes, 1987, 2017)

In 1934, their first clinical trial began at the University of Southern California. Sixteen cancer patients were a part of this initial process, all of them deemed terminally ill. Their treatments consisted of three-minute exposure to frequency therapy every three days, to allow the patients' bodies more time to dispose of the dead micro-organisms produced by the therapy—the remnants of the destroyed cancer cells. After three months of treatment, fourteen of the sixteen patients were certified as clinically cured. The other two were pronounced cured one month after the clinical trial concluded. (Lynes, 1987, 2017)

Sadly, major players in the pharmaceutical, medical, and insurance sectors worked tirelessly through the 1930s and 1940s to discredit Dr. Rife's work, including the American Medical Association, which threatened to revoke medical licenses from doctors who used Rife's machines. It is the consensus of many that a cure for disease as scientifically straightforward and effective as Dr. Rife's technology allowed for was simply bad for business. Why cure an illness, when you can offer endless surgeries, treatments, therapies, and medications… and charge high fees for it all. (Lynes, 1987, 2017) Public knowledge of Rife's work was fairly widespread for a short period of time. The Los Angeles Times wrote in 1940, "Organisms respond to certain wavelengths […] a theory carried to finality by bombarding disease germs with radio waves which are tuned to those of the tiny man-killers." The San Diego Tribune quoted Rife: "We can say that these waves […] have been shown to possess the power of devitalizing disease organisms, of 'killing' them, when tuned to the exact wavelength, or frequency, for each different organism." (Jones, 1938) But this attention was quashed by corporate greed. It would take decades before Rife's discoveries would be taken seriously again by the medical research community. Many promising studies have linked targeted electromagnetic energy therapies to curative results for cancer and many other ailments. One such study concluded that "Cancer-related frequencies appear to be tumor-specific and treatment with tumor-specific frequencies is feasible, well-tolerated and may have biological efficacy in patients with advanced cancer." (Barbault, 2009)

Rife's work, and the subsequent research into his discoveries, has inspired many technological developments in energy healing, most notably P.E.M.F. therapy devices, which emerged in the 1950s and have gone through many rounds of revision and reinvention through the decades since.

P.E.M.F. devices create small energy fields that stimulate cells in order to resolve cellular dysfunction. In essence, they are energy healing devices, and the frequencies they generate can be tailored to specific targets. Research into the effects of this sort of therapy has been extensive. In 1998, one technical report reviewed over two-hundred scientific papers on the effects of electromagnetic therapy. These papers examined this technology in relation to vascular disease, gastrointestinal disease, neurological disease, otorhinolaryngology, rheumatic disease, pediatrics, gynecology, oral medicine, immunity, dermatology, ophthalmology, surgery, inflammation, lung disease, reproduction, tumors, and many, many more. (Jerabeck; Pawluk, 1998) One of the authors of that report concluded in a subsequent journal article that "PEMFs of various kinds, strengths, and frequencies included have been found to have good results in a wide array of painful conditions. There is little risk when compared to the potential invasiveness of other therapies and the risk of toxicity, addiction, and complications from medications." (Pawluk, 2015) One of the most exciting fields in which P.E.M.F. devices have shown promise is in the treatment of depression. A recent study suggested that transcranial P.E.M.F. stimulation can "influence divergent neurobiological processes" in an antidepressant manner. (van Belkum, 2016)

ENERGY HEALING FOR ALL

I won't exhaust you with endless scientific examples, but a few more won't hurt. I want to paint the clearest picture possible that Qi and Qigong, or to put it more plainly, subtle energy and its mastery, are about so much more than highly trained and focussed masters. What these skilled practitioners have achieved and demonstrate with ease and precision has been developed through the deepest mindfulness, meditation, and practice. That's why so much of the research that has gone on in the past few decades is almost equally as impressive as their unique abilities—because it means that the average person can access the benefits of their mastery without having to dedicate a lifetime to crafting it. Scientists around the world are observing these masters, and digging deep into the chemistry, physics, and biology that make their feats possible, in an attempt to improve the lives of us all. There's a virtuousness to that endeavor that I find inspiring. It's that spirit of innovation and advancement that has motivated me to develop my own products in this space, and it's research like that which I'm sharing with you here that keeps me excited to keep pushing the boundaries in this field.

Take the University of Arizona's Dr. Ann Baldwin. Her work on biofield therapies (another term for energy healing therapies) concluded that exposure to electromagnetic fields "either directly or indirectly, amplifies autonomic arousal and energy, can reduce pain and improve range of motion." (Baldwin, 2017) Her earlier work focussed specifically on the practice of Reiki and was published in the Journal of Evidence-Based Complementary and Alternative Medicine. In that report, she suggested that Reiki was "as effective as manual manipulation physical therapy" in improving pain, and that "it would be beneficial for physical therapists to be trained in Reiki... so they could reduce the need for manual work on patients." (Baldwin, 2013)

Elsewhere, at the Susan Samueli Integrative Health Institute in California, Dr. Wayne B. Jonas conducted a review of various energy healing studies. On the topic of energy healing, the paper covered University of Michigan research that performed nineteen randomized, controlled trials on 1,122 patients. Eleven of the studies, or 58% of them, "reported statistically significant treatment effects," with the most positive outcomes reported in the alleviation of anxiety and pain. The same paper also looked at Qigong techniques studied at the Walter Reed Army Institute of Research, where it was shown that positive outcomes were seen in the treatment of immune modulation, as well as cellular and enzyme function. (Jonas, 2003)

And finally, in research that focussed on how energy healing can be used in the fight against dementia, which is a rapidly increasing issue for humanity as we live longer than ever before, studies have found that patients involved in trials experienced a reduction in both pain and anxiety associated with the disease, but also a decrease in heart rate, and an overall improvement in mood. Patients were also shown to participate more in social interaction, and many demonstrated an easing of their symptoms of depression and stress, as well as increased mental functioning, including memory. (Crawford, 2006; Baldwin, 2006, 2008; Friedman, 2011) In some cases, the beneficial effects lasted as long as a year after treatment in certain patients! (Shore, 2004) For so many of us nowadays, watching our elderly parents lose themselves in the fog of cognitive degenerative diseases like Alzheimer's and dementia can be a traumatizing experience, even more so for them as they suffer through the effects themselves. Imagine a world where the power of energy healing could help slow these diseases down or eradicate them entirely.

The science tells us it's possible... that so much more is possible. For mind. For body. For spirit.

CHAPTER IN REVIEW

In this chapter, we've traced the roots of Qi, Prana, Reiki – vital energy, subtle energy, life force... whatever you wish to call it. We looked at how learning to channel this energy form and master it through meditation and practice allows the user to balance the energy that resides within the body, and that which exists outside the body, in order to achieve health through balance and flow. At its peak mastery, subtle energy can be used to carry out monumental feats of healing (and much more, which we'll cover in later chapters). I shared the stories of several masters and how their abilities have been put to the test by rigorous scientific inquiry in recent decades, defying skepticism and Western medicine's long-held ignorance and greed. We've broken down some of the measurements and studies in this scientific inquiry and explored how the feats of the masters not only present challenges to accepted hard-science conclusions, theories, and laws, but also provide a blueprint for how to translate the powers of subtle energy forces into mainstream healing applications that we can all enjoy the benefits of.

As Dr. Claude Swanson explains, "A scientific revolution is underway as the effects of 'Life Force' are being demonstrated, documented and measured. It is like no other force known to science. It responds to consciousness and alters the other basic laws of physics." (Swanson, 2010) We know without a doubt that Qi is real. Its use and the effects of that use can be measured, and the results of those measurements tell us that subtle energy therapies can be preventative, responsive, and even curative. Energy healing is non-invasive, has virtually no side effects, and can be targeted to almost any health use, both physical and cognitive.

In the next chapter, I'll dig deeper into how subtle energy defies our current understanding of physics and how it can fill in the gaps in our knowledge.

Interested in transforming yourself with healing energy? You're not alone. Millions of people around the world have been turning to energy to better balance themselves and live a healthier life. Here are 5 reasons to consider healing yourself with the power of Qi:

1. *Energy healing relies on scientific principles.* You'll be making use of cutting-edge technology that is rooted in strong research and rigorous experimentation.

2. *Energy healing can be leveraged by anyone.* You don't need to be a guru or master—or even spiritual. An open mind is all you need, along with the right resources and devices, and you will experience the benefits.

3. ***Energy healing is great on its own or as a complementary therapy.*** Physical, mental, spiritual, and emotional benefits can all be experienced. In many cases, energy healing can complement or boost existing treatments you already engage in.

4. ***Energy healing is always accessible.*** At-home energy healing is always on-call. No appointments. No commutes. No waiting. You can maintain your flow of Qi at your own leisure. No limitations. No hassles.

5. ***Energy healing is holistic and homeostatic.*** Where most forms of therapy are either physical or mental, energy healing applies broadly to both body and mind.

Managing your Qi can maintain and restore well-being and overall health. It's natural, preventative, and responsive. And the advantages of Qi activation speak for themselves. Improve your circulation, increase your immunity, boost your stamina, accelerate your metabolism, generate new neural pathways, sharpen your focus and concentration, find deeper relaxation, and so much more. You'll experience total body rejuvenation and balance.

And by using the Qi Coil™ App, your transformation is made easy.

>>> **Visit www.QiCoilApp.com to download the app for free.**

CHAPTER 3

WE DON'T KNOW WHAT WE DON'T KNOW... OR DO WE?

THE GAPS IN OUR KNOWLEDGE

You've probably heard the expression "you don't know what you don't know". It's a clunky turn of phrase, maybe even a bit confusing… Essentially, it means there are things we don't know because we're not knowledgeable about them yet. These are the things that haven't crossed our minds, the things we haven't been interested in enough to dig deeper into, or the things that we've pretended aren't important because they don't fit in with the knowledge we already believe to be correct.

In a nutshell, this is what's wrong with modern science. The scientific method is highly effective at coming to conclusions, but its greatest shortcoming is its inability to factor in anomalies—things that challenge the *established* or *settled* scientific consensus. In some ways, this is helpful; it means not every theory or law can be upended or thrown out on a whim. We have to have an agreed-upon framework in order for certain things to be accomplished, after all. But in other ways, this means scientists are often held back or restricted from digging too deeply into new hypotheses, or even more troublingly, they are shunned, ridiculed, or blacklisted for daring to question the established doctrine in a given field of research.

Isn't it possible that what we don't know today is worth looking into because it will become what we <u>do know</u> tomorrow? Isn't that how we came to the settled science we operate with today in the first place? What if the anomalies hold all the secrets? What if the greatest anomaly of them all has been the foundation of ancient wisdom since the dawn of time? What if subtle energy, in all its forms, is begging us to acknowledge its presence and its powers?

There have always been scientists who have pushed the envelope, and gone down paths of research that others would never dare travel. In the last chapter, we covered some of their studies, in fact – research that proves there's something else at work within the universe, within ourselves. In some circles, this more adventurous, exploratory research is referred to as 'spiritual science', because it attempts to merge the ever-growing body of subtle energy research with the entrenched hard sciences that like to pretend such things don't exist.

Over the past few decades, it's become increasingly clear through accumulating evidence that science as a whole is nearing a tipping point. On the other side, through acceptance and curiosity, humanity will take great leaps forward, the likes of which we haven't taken since the days of Albert Einstein, whose theories of relativity and quantum mechanics revolutionized the academic world.

Galileo, Copernicus, Bruno, Darwin, Einstein, Planck… What do these great minds all have in common? At the time of their initial revelations, the mainstream scientific communities around them thought they were crazy. Their theories and ideas were mocked, shunned, or rejected out of hand. In some cases, scientists with new ideas that challenged the status quo, the orthodox, or even the religious elites, were threatened with torture or put to death. When the Church didn't like his theory of gravity and acceleration, Galileo basically said, "Oh, never mind. My bad!" and pretended he'd made a mistake in his calculations. Giordano Bruno, who correctly hypothesized that stars were actually distant suns like our own, had more conviction than Galileo did… and as a result, he was burned at the stake for sticking to his guns. (Mendoza, 1995) As Max Planck once said of his own theories about quantum mechanics being ignored for years, "Science advances funeral by funeral." Sometimes the old guard needs to die off before newer ideas are given a fighting chance.

But how does this happen? Why is the potential of ancient wisdom and knowledge—of subtle energy, being left to the sidelines? Astronomer Halton Arp has a solid perspective on this matter. He believes that the process of peer review, which once held scientific research to account and ensured that calculations and experiments were carried out with failsafe attention to detail, has been hijacked by arrogance, selfishness, and economic priorities. In his essay entitled *What Has Science Come To?*, he says, "Originally, a reviewer could help an author improve his article by pointing out errors in calculation, references, clarity, etc., but scientists, in their fervid attachment to their own theories, have now mostly used their selection as a referee to reject publication of any result that would be unfavorable to their own personal commitment… The press, of course, only reports news from established academic centers that have a strong financial and prestige interest in glorifying the status quo. The result is that real investigative science is mostly now an underground activity." (Arp, 2000)

Especially in our modern era, where the concept of *fact* and *truth* is being distorted by social media, conspiracy theories, and a strong distrust in government and institutions, this insistence to *trust the science* at all costs no matter what is holding us back as a society and as a civilization is dangerous and unhelpful. It's understandable that in the face of so much mis- and disinformation, we would default to a hardline approach to scientific agreement, but it's counterproductive for us to not explore new angles, opportunities, and ideas. It will only set us back in the long run if we're not willing to be more open-minded and adventurous.

Prior to these modern information wars of the last few years, the scientific community, particularly in the field of physics, was steadfast in its quest to uncover a *final theory*—a set of laws that would explain the universe with certainty. (Swanson, 2003) But pesky side inquiries kept bubbling to the surface. Research on the fringes carried out by brave and curious physicists was testing the boundaries of the status quo, revealing unexplainable anomalies that bring into question what we think we know to be true. For the longest time, the academic elite has been able to label this body of fringe research as too wild, too imaginative, and too *out there*... but the dam is breaking. With each year, these new, exploratory avenues of research are becoming clearer, more substantiated, and louder. They're becoming too reasonable and evidence-based to ignore. They bring into question the *final theory* that had been coming together and threaten to break apart the foundational laws of science as we know them.

I want to take you through several of these lines of research—these so-called *radical ideas*. We won't get too technical. This is physics after all! But I will outline the basics so you can have a strong basis of understanding to work from and draw your own conclusions. I believe that in the face of this science, you will be left with a clear perspective: that we don't know what we don't know... but maybe we do...

DARK MATTER / DARK ENERGY

"It is an embarrassment that the dominant forms of matter in the universe are hypothetical..." These are the words of Princeton University's Jim Peebles, a professor of physics. (Swanson, 2003) What is he talking about? For much of the 20th century, scientists believed they had crafted what is often referred to as the 'theory of everything'—an all-encompassing framework of theoretical physics that accounts for and connects every physical aspect of our universe. (Weinberg, 2011) The two major fields that form this theory of everything are general relativity and quantum mechanics. A unifying theory that explains the universe as neat and tidy, and most of all, explainable, is the holy grail of physics, and for a while, general relativity and quantum mechanics seemed to overlap in such a way that scientists were left satisfied with themselves. They believed there were only a few missing pieces to the puzzle left to uncover.

But then an unexpected piece came along in their quest. It wasn't the piece they were looking for. In fact, it blew the puzzle apart again. We call this piece 'dark matter' or 'dark energy'. As it turns out, at least 90% of the matter in the universe is undefined and unexplainable (BBC News Online, 2000). In other words, we don't know what it is, and we don't know how it works. In many cases, we only know it exists because of an absence of observable matter; there's something causing gravitational effects, effects that are strong enough to bend light. Another way to describe dark matter is as a region of space where there is insufficient visible matter to explain the gravitational pull being measured in that region. (Swanson, 2010)

We got our first visual taste of this in the year 2000. Throughout the 1990s, astronomers were compiling the first-ever glimpses of dark matter over a two-square-degree expanse of sky (roughly the size of the full moon from the perspective of standing on Earth). Using the Canada-France-Hawaii Telescope on Mauna Kea in Hawaii, the light from 200,000 galaxies was analyzed by Dr. Yannick Mellier and his team. As you can see in the images included here, what they observed resembled a network or web. It would later be dubbed a 'cosmic web'. These web links, or filaments, appear to connect the galaxies to one another—a remnant from the Big Bang perhaps. (Swanson, 2010)

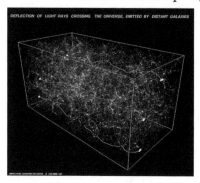

Figure 3.1 *(Source: NIC Group, S. Colombi, IAP)* This figure shows the measurement of dark matter in a region of sky a billion lightyears long. The larger spots represent visible galaxies, and the stringy filaments represent the detected dark matter. It was found that the dark matter forms filaments which connect the visible galaxies.

The filaments or cosmic web seen in these images, represent the absence of traditional forms of matter. And just look how much absence there is! It's actually quite mind-blowing. Since this first glimpse, a mountain of evidence has grown to document dark matter. Astrophysicist David Spergel, of Princeton and the University of Maryland, suggests that these observations present proof that dark matter is something different to the protons and neutrons that we understand so well, and use as the basis of our understanding of how matter is supposed to function and

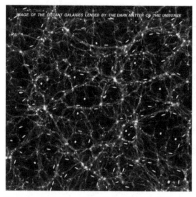

Figure 3.2 *(Source: NIC Group, S. Colombi, IAP)* Close-up of the previous image.

behave. (Spergel, 2000) If it's different, or *other*, then not only are we nowhere near as close to the theory of everything we thought we had created, we almost have to start from scratch.

The evidence seems to suggest quite convincingly that galaxies would behave differently if there wasn't a large amount of unseen matter at work—that they would move in ways they currently don't. It is believed that some galaxies would never even have formed in the first place if it weren't for the effects of dark matter. (Siegfried, 1999)

It is for this reason that physicists are coming to terms with the idea that dark matter must be composed of subatomic elementary particles that we have yet to discover—particles that are not composed of smaller particles. Put more simply, dark matter must be a kind of foundational building block of the universe. (Braibant, 2012; Copi, 1995) This is a wild revelation for the scientific community. It's hard to put into words just how much dark matter shatters our core understanding of how the universe operates, even how it was formed. Around the world, research into determining exactly how dark matter works is being undertaken, but so far, none has succeeded in forming a complete theory that meets the standard of a *theory of everything*. (Bertone, 2005)

It's possible that the Russians might be the closest to figuring it all out, however. And they may have started that process decades ago, as far back as a century, in fact. Physicists like Ivan Shakhparanov and Gennady Shipov have led some of the most cutting-edge research in this field, and it is their belief that dark matter may be subtle energy itself. (Shakhparanov, 1998, 2001; Shipov, 2004) Russian studies of subtle energy have long shown that this special energy form, what they call *torsion*, can, in fact, have a similar effect as gravity. Could it be then, that the mysterious, unaccountable gravitational pull of dark matter is really just subtle energy at work? As you'll recall, some scientists believe that subtle energy, or Qi, is a foundational building block of the universe—an elemental particle, if you will. Subtle energy, after all, is a transfer or flow of energy from one entity to another. Dark matter seems to operate in a similar fashion, exerting force from one entity to another.

Russian experiments during the first half of the 1900s suggested that torsion could be stored and transferred from one object to another (Swanson, 2010). This was supported by German scientist Karl von Reichenbach, whose work in biological magnetism also observed a peculiar energy form transferring from substance to substance. He called this energy form Od, after the Norse god Odin, a 'vital force' that permeated and connected all living things. (von Reichenbach, 1850; Vassilitos, 2000) Could dark matter be… a *life force*? Could it be universal Qi? Let's explore this torsion concept a little further…

TORSION

Russian astrophysicist Nikolai Kozyrev is known for many theories, but what interests me most about his work is what he called the 'density of time'. He believed that physical forces could alter the rate at which time passes. (Swanson, 2008) He came to this conclusion while studying the formation of binary stars: two stars that orbit each other. Kozyrev noticed something strange: the stars' behaviour couldn't be explained by the known principles of the day. When binary stars start out, you see, they are different sizes and share very few characteristics. Over time, the smaller of the two stars starts to resemble the larger one, but Kozyrev didn't think basic force fields could create this kind of mirroring effect so quickly. This led him to believe that some unseen or unknown energy force must be at work. He believed the larger stars in the pairings were affecting the smaller ones not just through gravity, but through the energy of time itself. "It's almost as if the stars are communed by telepathy," he said. (Ostrander, 1970) This *telepathic* force seemed to work in a twisting fashion. He called it 'torsion'.

PROCESSES WHICH INCREASE ENTROPY: "EMIT TIME"
"RIGHT HANDED TORSION"
ENERGY OR ORDER LEAVING THE SYSTEM

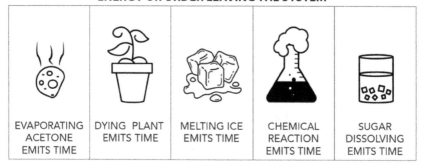

EVAPORATING ACETONE EMITS TIME	DYING PLANT EMITS TIME	MELTING ICE EMITS TIME	CHEMICAL REACTION EMITS TIME	SUGAR DISSOLVING EMITS TIME

Figure 3.3 *(Source: Swanson, 2008, license unknown)*
Right-handed torsion is explained visually.

So what is torsion? And how does it work? To be honest, it's pretty complicated. Far too complicated to get technical. Essentially, it's a twisting energy force that emits time when it spins in one direction (right-handed torsion) and absorbs time when it spins in the opposite direction (left-handed torsion).

Kozyrev's work was focussed on right-handed torsion—the kind that emits time, so I'll start there. When the energy of matter is used up, the behavior of the particles becomes randomized and diffused. This process is often called 'entropy', which basically means a breakdown of order or structure. In Figure 3.3, you can see some examples of this: evaporating, melting, dissolving... Imagine a log being burned: its solid structure is reduced to ash and smoke. The order and structure of the log are broken down and dispersed into the air as energy. Many physicists believe that increased entropy explains the basic passage of time: the emission of time. (Swanson, 2010) Kozyrev found this explanation unsustainable, however, because it would mean that when all the energy in the universe is spent or used up, the universe itself would eventually diffuse and die. He didn't believe in this inevitable burnout of the cosmos. "Stars die and are born again. The Universe sparkles with inexhaustible variety," he said. (Kozyrev, 1958) In his mind, there will always be energy and matter developing. If a star dies, where does all its energy go? It can't just be gone. It must go *somewhere*.

PROCESSES WHICH DECREASE ENTROPY: "ABSORB TIME"
"LEFT HANDED TORSION"
PUTTING ENERGY OR ORDER INTO SYSTEM

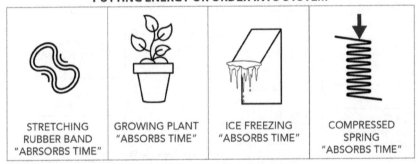

| STRETCHING RUBBER BAND "ABRSORBS TIME" | GROWING PLANT "ABSORBS TIME" | ICE FREEZING "ABSORBS TIME" | COMPRESSED SPRING "ABSORBS TIME" |

Figure 3.4 *(Source: Swanson, 2008, license unknown)*
Left-handed torsion is explained visually.

He believed spent energy is absorbed somewhere else and used to develop new matter elsewhere. This process is called left-handed torsion. The energy works in the opposite direction and has the opposite effect. Take a look at Figure 3.4. Tension, biological growth, freezing, and compression are all examples of left-handed torsion, or the absorption of time. Particles are solidifying, strengthening, and developing. Entropy decreases and slows. Order and structure occur. According to Kozyrev, the energy that allows water to freeze or a plant to grow is just recycled energy that was used up and exhausted somewhere else in the universe.

He theorized that when these processes happen, the density of time itself is changed: time is emitted in one place... and absorbed in another. The alteration of time radiates outwardly in a twisting wave (right-handed torsion) that will inevitably be absorbed somewhere else. When the absorption process occurs at the receiving location, the reverse takes place: entropy decreases and the diffused energy re-concentrates (left-handed torsion). This flies against traditionally accepted physics, in that energy is never truly spent; it simply reconstitutes itself somewhere else in the universe. There is a balance of energy, not exhaustion of it. It's the ultimate, intergalactic recycling program!

With this framework in mind, Kozyrev concluded that if time has a twisting energy force, then space likely does as well. Therefore, particles (matter itself) must be subject to torsion as well, including *elemental particles*. As I'm sure you'll recall, I talked about these earlier. Particles have a unique, natural spin to them. Each time a particle speeds up, it produces a twisting effect of its own. Kozyrev believed that particles themselves exert torsion, so it makes perfect sense then that when particles are charged and produce an electromagnetic energy wave, those waves would be *torsion energy waves*.

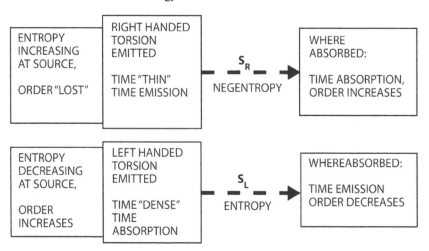

Figure 3.5 *(Source: Swanson, 2008, license unknown)* When entropy (energy diffusion and dispersion) is increased, the lost 'information' is conserved and reconstructed or absorbed somewhere else in the universe. Energy is never truly lost or spent. It ebbs and flows through the universe.

Kozyrev believed this flow of energy to be virtually instantaneous. (Swanson, 2010) After all, time has to exist simultaneously—all at once, everywhere. He didn't think that this necessarily contradicted the theory of general relativity (the laws of gravity), but he did think that torsion allows for "instantaneous connection through time". (Kozyrev, 1976) His conclusions have been extensively tested and studied by Russian scientists in the years since his death. Torsion is also backed up by the Synchronized Universal Model (S.U.M.). The S.U.M. assumes that all particles interact with one another, essentially operating on Mach's Principle: the motion of matter in one place affects the motion of matter in another.

Instantaneous connection through time. It suggests that electrons in one place are tethered in space and time to electrons in another distant place by photons. Hmm… That sounds familiar, right? Remember the *cosmic web* from Dr. Mellier's observations of dark matter using the telescope in Hawaii that we discussed earlier? What if those filaments that he and his team reported—the ones that connected galaxies are really these tethers of virtual photons: torsion energy?

As Dr. Claude Swanson notes in his 2003 book *The Synchronized Universe,* "Momentum and energy that is created here is absorbed there and vice versa. The local, nearby electron does not dance alone. It is therefore not a random motion that it undergoes. If we could somehow know the motions of the particles at the other end, which are in the distant matter of stars, then we could PREDICT the detailed motions of the local electron as it zigs and zags. Of course, practically speaking this is an impossible task. But the idea that the motions of local particles and distant particles are connected is an important and fundamental insight." The key word there is connected. I agree with those who have proposed that the cosmic web is the invisible secret of an interconnected universe. A subtle energy (torsion energy) ripples through space and time, simultaneously affecting all matter. Qi is everywhere and everything. Its ebb and flow are endless, but equally balanced within the universe because wherever it is spent or exhausted, it is absorbed and recreated elsewhere. Yin and yang. A universal harmony.

In the 1950s, physicists Chen Ning Yang and Robert Mills produced what would become known as the Yang-Mills theories. Virtually every theory of physics that has been developed since the 1950s fits within the parameters of the Yang-Mills theories. This includes the Standard Model of particle physics, which is the currently accepted theory of how matter functions. (Oerter, 2006; Nielsen, 2007) As it happens, torsion energy fields obey the laws of physics that the Yang-Mills theories propose. This work essentially confirms Kozyrev's calculations. These fields "can alter the rate of time and produce stable energy forms without the need for matter." (Swanson, 2008) Without the need for matter. The localized and distant energy projections of subtle energy masters are exactly this: stable energy without the need for matter. When you start to see these patterns and connections, whole worlds of possibility start to become apparent.

If we assume these theories to be true, then we understand clearly the relevant characteristics of ancient energy forms like Qi. They operate with the same polarity that Mach's Principle establishes: yin and yang. A flow created in one direction or place exists in the opposite direction somewhere else. Balancing it to one's own advantage and favor—that's the key to living in harmony, and the physics backs it up. Dark matter, dark energy, torsion... whatever you want to call it. It is subtle energy at work. Kozyrev was right: there exists a truly cosmic, universal energy force. And it's one that the mainstream scientific community has been ignoring for decades. Let's look at another few examples to see what else the mainstream is choosing to ignore...

GRAVITY

For the longest time, scientists have had to grapple with shortcomings in the established laws of gravity, otherwise known as the theory of general relativity. There are weaknesses that most mainstream physicists like to pretend aren't there for the sake of not having to dig deeper or admit that we can't explain everything. Take the bizarre irregularities that occur during solar eclipses... When a solar eclipse occurs, a phenomenon known as the Allais Effect transpires.

Figure 3.6 *(Source: TimeandDate.com, license unknown)*
Representation of the sun obstructed by the moon, creating a solar eclipse.

On June 30, 1954, French physicist Maurice Allais noticed something wrong when he was observing a solar eclipse. Some of his measurement devices (like Foucault pendulums, and gravimeters) behaved in ways that couldn't be explained by the physics of the time. (Hecht, 2010) In 1959, during another solar eclipse, and using a special paraconical pendulum of his own invention, Allais observed similar instrument misbehavior. (Allais, I and II, 1959) Essentially, the instruments and devices, which are dependent on gravity to measure accurately, veer off their trajectory during an eclipse, demonstrating detectable deviations in their normal and expected behaviour.

As he would later explain, the movement of his pendulum simply can't be explained by the theory of relativity as we know it. "My experiments correspond to a dynamic phenomenon." (Allais, 1999) Something is bending the Sun's gravitational field during solar eclipses. Similar results were observed by Dr. Leonid Savrov in Mexico and Brazil during eclipses in 1991 and 1994 respectively. Of the bizarre instrument behaviour, he said

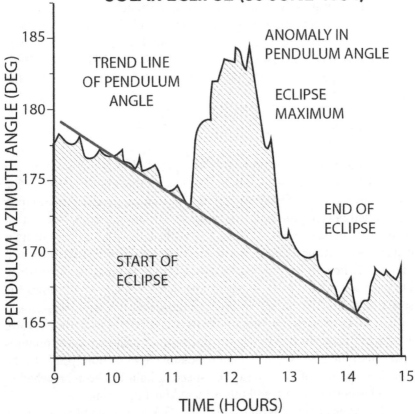

GRAVITATIONAL ANOMALY DURING SOLAR ECLIPSE (30 JUNE 1954)

Figure 3.7 *(Source: Swanson, 2010, license unknown)* The hump in the middle of the graph indicates the anomalous behaviour of a Foucault pendulum during a solar eclipse.

"It seems that we have some kind of special effect." (Savrov, 1995, 1997, 2005) In 1970, when they noticed irregularities in the way their pendulum operated during a solar eclipse, physicists Erwin Saxl and Mildred Allen concluded that the theory of gravity as we know it needs to be modified. (Saxl, Allen, 1971) Surely, if so many scientists from all over the globe have witnessed this unique and unexplainable phenomenon, and come to the same conclusion that we need to

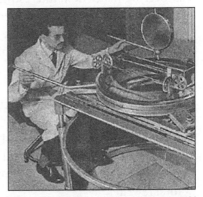

Figure 3.8 *(Source: Wikipedia, 2005: Public Domain)* Jacques Bourgeot operating the Allais paraconical pendulum, taken by Maurice Allais.

investigate further, we should be taking their observations seriously, no?

Could this be a case of subtle energy at work? Perhaps this deviation in the effects of gravity is just a recycling of spent energy elsewhere in the universe presenting itself during eclipses: a balance of energy flow, yin and yang. With so many scientists reporting the same effect, why isn't the scientific community exploring this further? The Allais Effect may well be a gateway to proving subtle energy's foundational role in the *theory of everything.*

SPEED OF LIGHT

It has been the accepted bedrock gospel of physics that nothing can travel faster than the speed of light. But what if that's not true? In a 2002 paper released by Professor Raymond Chiao and his colleagues, no time was wasted burying the lead. Their paper's outline started by saying that their experiments confirmed their predictions that the velocity of light can exceed 'c'. (Chiao, 2002) In physics, 'c' is the shorthand for the speed of light. By how much faster did they exceed it, you may be wondering? I'm glad you asked. They managed to reach a velocity of 1.7 times the speed of light! The nature of their experiments has been reproduced several times over by different scientists around the world. They involve a complex usage of barriers and reflections in order to move photons faster than the laws of physics say is possible. I won't bore you with the calculations, but suffice it to say, the speed of light has been breached in isolated experimentation and this is incredibly important.

That same paper goes on to conclude, "We have been blinded by our misconceptions, and thereby have been prevented from exploring and discovering many new, interesting, and possibly important, phenomena, which could have been discovered long ago. Some of these are only now being uncovered, and some of these phenomena may in fact lead to important applications..." (Chiao, 2002) Chiao himself first explored faster-than-light experiments in the 1990s. And others in that era also sensed that something was off in the accepted status quo. "There are several serious possibilities for real FTL [faster-than-light] which have been proposed in the scientific literature." (Gibbs, 1997) Even further back than that, Albert Einstein himself admitted that the laws of light speed "cannot claim unlimited validity." (Einstein, 1921) In simpler terms, the laws aren't etched in stone; they may be subject to exceptions or even a total rewrite.

As Professor Emeritus of Physics at the University of Washington John G. Cramer has said, "It seems to me, however, that this is no longer a matter of theories or definitions, but an experimental question that should be treated as such." (Cramer, 1995) In other words, if such an unflappable scientific principle as the speed of light can be brought into question, then surely we owe it to ourselves to actively pursue new revelations through scientific research. Could those cosmic web filaments connecting galaxies be pathways through which the speed of light can be broken perhaps? Could the energy projection of Qi masters be faster than light—it has been repeatedly observed to be instantaneous, after all. The answers to questions like these should be exciting avenues of academic exploration that could lead to new frontiers in science.

COLD FUSION

In the 1980s, electrochemists Martin Fleischmann and Stanley Pons announced to the world that they had used electrolysis devices to generate nuclear processes—or reactions, resulting in unexplainable, excess energy. They claimed their devices did this at room temperature. (Fleischmann, Pons, 1989) Traditional nuclear fusion, as you'll no doubt be aware (i.e. how stars burn and nuclear bombs and reactors operate in order to generate energy), is an exceptionally heat-intensive process. It's wildly hot!

While several variations in method have developed since these 1989 experiments, the original tests worked like this: a cold fusion cell consisting of two electrodes was suspended in a solution of palladium and heavy water. The electrodes were connected to a power source in order to facilitate electrical transmission between the electrodes. (Anderson, 2009) The surprising result in Fleischmann and Pons' original

Figure 3.9 (Source: Zuma Press Inc., Alamy, Photoarena, license unknown) Pons and Fleischmann demonstrate their device in 1989.

experiments was an excess generation of heat energy beyond what should have occurred. This was the shocker that turned heads around the world. It shouldn't have been possible. After the initial chemical reaction, the energy flow should have stopped, but it carried on, as only a nuclear reaction can. It also produced fusion by-products, just like a nuclear reaction would.

As they wrote in their paper in 1989, "Evidently, it is necessary to reconsider the quantum mechanics of electrons," and, "the bulk of the energy release is due to a hitherto unknown nuclear process..." These results shook the scientific world upon their release, with many mainstream figures and organizations loudly denying that cold fusion was even possible. The United States Department of Energy funded several rapid inquiries that same year and joined the doubtful opposition within the scientific community. But even with such high-level disbelief and suppression at work, other scientists kept researching cold fusion as viable. Since then, over five-hundred labs around the world have independently replicated Fleischmann and Pons' results. (Swanson, 2010) This field of research has come to be known as low-energy nuclear reactions (L.E.N.R.), and a dedicated few have continued exploring the potential of cold fusion as an alternate source of energy production. Even the E.P.R.I. (Electric Power Research Institute), a non-profit organization funded by American electric utilities corporations, invested $10 million into evaluating cold fusion. Their analysis confirmed that the excess energy generation using cold fusion devices was "at levels too large to be chemical transformations." The energy levels they evaluated were off the charts, exceeding what was thought traditionally possible. (Swanson, 2010)

If you're still wondering why this discovery is so monumental, it's that fusion is one of the most powerful ways to generate energy. It's why nuclear power plants were once thought to be the future of energy production. If there's another way to generate it, without the same levels of heat or the dangers that come along with the process as we know it today, it could revolutionize the way we produce and consume energy: potentially giving humanity unlimited energy!

Solid state fusion experimental apparatus

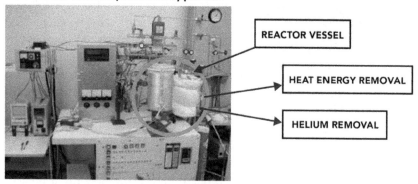

Figure 3.10 *(Source: Rothwell, Storms, 2008, license unknown)*
Arata's experimental device from his public demonstration in 2008.

Recent research has continued to prove the value of cold fusion as a viable solution to our energy problems. Japanese professor Yoshiaki Arata used gas compression devices rather than electrolysis and produced the same excess energy results. He conducted public experiments in 2008 at Osaka University to showcase his 'solid fusion' (or cold fusion) device, which did not require the use of an energy input—a first-of-its-kind test.

In the accompanying paper issued at their demonstration, Arata and his partner Zhang stated, "It is considered that the solid nuclear fusion described above is useful for an energy source for homes, cars, ships, airplanes and the like. Quickly implementing measures is desired in view of the current air pollution problem. It is possible that a further new science and new industry are to be developed." (Arata, 2008) Akito Takahashi, a fellow Japanese physicist who observed Arata's public demonstration told New Energy Times, "Arata and Zhang demonstrated very successfully the generation of continuous excess energy…", carrying on to say, "This demonstration showed that the method is highly reproducible." (Krivit, 2008)

Talbot Chubb, a noted Naval Research Laboratory physicist from the United States, reviewed these 2008 tests as well, and emphasized the "unique importance for demonstrating to the world that cold fusion is a real phenomenon." He found it remarkable that no electrical input was required and concluded that this surely meant that an "unidentified new physics" was being developed. He doubled down on the importance of this being a true nuclear fusion reaction. "I say nuclear because no plausible large magnitude alternative energy source has been identified," adding, "This is strong evidence for cold fusion reality." (Chubb, 2008)

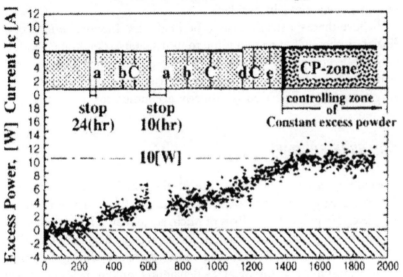

Figure 3.11 (Source: Chubb, 2008 c/o Arata, 2002, license unknown) This graph demonstrates roughly 10 watts of excess heat power, which carried on for three weeks during one of Arata's device tests.

Arata and Zhang made a specific effort to point out the ecological benefits of cold fusion. (Arata, 2008) This is partly why this research is so groundbreaking. Not only is it demonstrating large energy generation potential that defies the accepted rules of physics, but it could also help solve our global energy crisis if scaled up. L.E.N.R. research expert Steven Krivit promotes this angle as one of the most promising benefits, pointing out that cold fusion offers hope for practical energy production that poses no major health threats, and produces no greenhouse gasses. (Krivit, 2008)

Let's not mince words: the downplay and dismissal of this tremendous breakthrough research by the scientific community and fossil fuel corporations suggests very clearly that these parties are likely working hard to prevent this research from going mainstream for various profit-driven motives! And let's not forget the military motive of secrecy and weaponization of technology. We know that some of the most advanced experiments are carried out by militaries of major powers around the world. It serves their interests to deny that a technology like cold fusion is functional... or even real, because they can use it for themselves rather than to help humanity. Consider the strange aerial phenomenon recently declassified by the Pentagon. Are the bizarre flying vehicles in those videos and the testimonies of the pilots who recorded them proof of alien aircraft... or is it possible that advanced cold fusion engines are powering top-secret experimental planes already? Maybe we've already witnessed the future of aviation... by accident.

I believe there's a strong case to be made that the *unidentified* new *physics* that Talbot was alluding to in his analysis of Arata's work is simply subtle energy. Qi. It's what all of these unexplained phenomena have in common. An energy form that works at the particle level: a subtle energy that simply hasn't been properly accounted for, recognized, or measured.

CHAPTER IN REVIEW

Claude Swanson believes we are at the forefront of a paradigm shift. "In the early days of a scientific revolution, the evidence is always incomplete." He points to the likes of Michael Faraday, whose meticulous work entrenched electric and magnetic forces, and the Benjamin Franklins of the world, who bravely and dangerously flew kites during lightning storms. (Swanson, 2003) Are we in the Benjamin Franklin stage of this next great revolution, waving our kite around to see if lightning will strike? As Swanson jokes, mankind spent thousands of years not being able to explain casual electrical shocks—like when we touch a doorknob after walking across a carpet. We don't know what we don't know until we know it.

We've looked at dark matter and dark energy, and how we can't see them in action, but by virtue of the measurable absences they leave and effects they create on other matter and forces, we know they exist. We've discussed the predominantly Russian-led field of torsion research, which suggests that a cosmic, universal energy force exists and binds everything together—potentially subtle energy itself. We reviewed the ways in which the laws of gravity have come into question, how solar eclipses seem to bend gravity in ways we can't explain. We explored the speed of light being broken in exciting experiments, and how even Einstein himself had a hunch that light speed may not be conclusively constant. And finally, we dug into cold fusion's unexplained energy generation, and what it could mean for the future of nuclear power.

It's entirely likely that the shortcomings we have in explaining some of the rule-breaking we've observed in this chapter are simply down to our uncertainty about how to properly measure and quantify what we're observing. Electricity, gravity, nuclear forces: scientists simply didn't possess the tools and technology necessary to attain a solid grasp of these fields (and so many others) … until they did. We don't know what we don't know. Perhaps it is even that we can't know what we don't know unless we're brave enough to embrace the anomalies, irregularities and exceptions to the rules, brave enough to examine the seemingly unexplainable, and acknowledge that science is a living, breathing process, one that needs to take deep breaths of fresh air from time to time and not always give in to and settle for the status quo. We can make observations, measurements, and continue to engage in experimentation until the puzzle pieces start to fit together. By understanding the basic characteristics and qualities of what we observe, we build a body of evidence and knowledge, and the puzzle starts to provide the clarity we're missing. Eventually, some bright mind will come along out of nowhere and deliver the final missing pieces. The image will become complete. We'll have a true *theory of everything*.

What seems to bind all of the rule-breaking I've outlined in this chapter is the same core building block that this book is all about: subtle energy. Qi. There are energy forces at work in all of the strange and curious examples we've gone through. I keep coming back to this concept of a cosmic web. It's the puzzle I think we've been moving toward solving, piece by piece, for thousands of years. Ancient civilizations were intuitive enough to understand that some other force was at work, both within and around us. Did they come to this insight and wisdom on their own? Was it shared with them by some otherworldly, cosmic entity or interstellar visitor? Who's to say… What excites me most is that we have enough knowledge, both ancient and contemporary, to see that subtle energy forms carry enormous power. We may not understand the exact mechanisms by which they operate yet, but we do have a strong enough grasp to engage with these revelations in the same honest ways that Qi and other subtle energy masters have, and *still do* to this day. We've observed their feats, and seen their results.

We should use the mysteries that the gaps in our technical understanding present, such as those discussed in this chapter, as catalysts to dig deeper and push further toward not only scientific revolution and a general paradigm shift, but equally, and perhaps more importantly, toward a revolution and paradigm shift of body, mind, and spirit. I see this as a new, deeper spiritual science. The science of Qi energy.

In the next chapter, we'll explore what this bold new frontier looks like, how many are already pioneers of that exploration. We'll take a look at where the gaps are closing in, and clarity is prevailing.

Just like the gaps in the scientific record, most of us experience gaps in the maintenance of our bodies, minds, and spirits. We lead busy lives, complicated by so many distractions. It can be hard to dial it all in, concentrate on the things that matter, and focus on filling those gaps in our personal well-being. But these gaps can be filled. And future gaps can be prevented. So often the things we feel we're missing are a result of poor Qi flow and balance. So why not automate your Qi energy—make it a part of your daily routine without even having to think about it.

With Qi Energy AI, you can send and receive the healing and protection of sub-space subtle energy to or from any phone or physical location. Using distinct energy signatures, you'll harness the power of personal quantum entanglement. Experience increased brain longevity, boosted recovery times, expanded consciousness, deeper sleep and meditation, sharper cognitive clarity, greater abundance, and so much more!

>>> **Visit <u>www.OiEnergy.ai</u> to experience the world's most powerful automated Quantum Energy.**

SCAN ME!

CHAPTER 4

A NEW FRONTIER: THE FIFTH FORCE

I f we really are at the dawn of a scientific revolution, what does the new frontier look like? In the previous chapter, I outlined some of the examples of scientific weaknesses and shortcomings that currently face the scientific community. Anomalies that can't be explained by our current grasp of the science. As I pointed out, the common denominator between those examples was, of course, subtle energy. But maybe you noticed something else in those examples. Perhaps you picked up on the *types* of forces at work. If you did, you'll have noticed that there really aren't that many kinds of forces at play within the field of physics. In fact, as the science currently stands, or rather, as far as the mainstream scientific community has been willing to divulge, there are only four of these forces, or interactions as they're also called. These forces/interactions are referred to as *fundamental*. Naturally, I'm going to tell you what lies beyond… the fifth force… but to create a solid footing of understanding, let's take a quick Physics 101 look at the core four.

These fundamental four forces establish the basis and foundation for all known physical interactions in the universe: gravitational, electromagnetic, strong nuclear, and weak nuclear. (Braibant, 2011)

Main properties of the four fundamental interactions at low energy

Force	Strength (adimensional constant)	Range (cm)	Subjected particles	Exchanged (boson) particle	Mass of the exchanged bosons	Spin ^{Parity} of the exchanged bosons
Strong	0.1 *short distances*					
	1 *large distances*	10^{-13}	Quarks, gluons	8 gluons	0	1^-
Electro-magnetic	1/137	∞	Charged particles	Photon	0	1^-
Weak	$1.027 \cdot 10^{-5}$	$<10^{-15}$	Leptons, quarks	Vector intermediate bosons ($W^{\pm}$, Z^0)	80.6 GeV 91.2 GeV	1^+ 1^- [a]
Gravitation	$5.9 \cdot 10^{-5}$	∞	All	Graviton	0	2^+

[a] In weak interaction, parity is violated

Figure 4.1 The main properties of the four fundamental forces.

In terms of how these forces present themselves, it's the gravitational and electromagnetic ones that you and I see and experience in real-time all around us on a daily basis. Gravity obviously keeps us connected to the Earth; you see it in action every time you drop something or fall down. Electromagnetic forces govern every electrical and digital experience we have from turning on a light to scrolling through Instagram, to getting a static shock when we touch a doorknob. Meanwhile, weak and strong nuclear interactions take place at a scale we rarely see with the naked eye, but they make our reality as we know it possible; they produce all the tiny, subatomic and nuclear interactions that govern the universe. The strong force holds the nuclei of atoms together, for example, and the weak force is what causes some atoms to break apart. (Wilford, 1987) As far as we've observed, or are willing to admit, it is assumed that these forces cannot be reduced to more basic physical interactions. They are the base-level forces that serve as the blueprint of the physical order of the universe.

FUNDAMENTAL FORCES OF NATURE

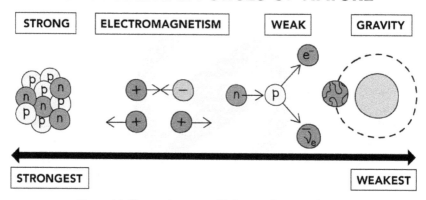

Figure 4.2 (*Source: Astronomy Trek, 2016, license unknown*)
The four fundamental forces.

If we dig just another layer deeper in your standard-issue textbook, we would discover that the fundamental interactions are described as *fields* by the mathematicians who calculate how these forces work. The gravitational field is distinct from the others and is derived from the curvature of spacetime. The other three forces are what we call *quantum fields,* and their interactions are derived from elemental particles, which I've touched on earlier in this book.

Most physicists will tell you that all four fundamental forces/ interactions are interconnected and that under certain extreme circumstances, like the intensity of the Big Bang, for example, all four act as a unified force at the smallest subatomic scale. This is referred to as the Planck scale and is considered the minimum limit at which the laws of physics can feasibly operate. Any smaller an interaction and it would seem as though the spacetime structure of the universe starts to break up. (Swanson, 2003) In other words, at such a small scale, we don't yet have the tools or calculations to explain what forces or interactions are at work. The inability of physicists to explain this has always been one of the leading motivators to pursue and develop a unified theory—a *theory of everything*. But as close as we've come, with some scientists more or less acting as though we've already found it, we still haven't fully gotten there.

I like to point out this shortcoming in the framework of the four fundamental forces because it opens up the obvious question that you've probably already started asking yourself:

What other forces are at work then?

What are we missing?

A FIFTH FORCE

I'm always encouraged by brave scientists, those who dare to explore new possibilities—the ones who aren't afraid of ridicule or rejection because they know that even if their theories are proven incorrect, the research was still worth the effort to narrow down their idea, and maybe lead them to the right answer in the end. The search for the fifth force is perhaps the most important quest in modern science, but it remains explored by a considerable few. Thankfully, this effort has been picking up speed in the last few decades, and I believe that the outcome will help explain the anomalies I outlined in Chapter 3... and so much more!

So what can we say about this elusive fifth force at the moment? Well, for starters, quite a few researchers believe it is weaker than the electromagnetic and nuclear forces, and that it is likely similar in strength to the gravitational force. Some physicists believe it is slightly stronger than gravity, which would make it about as strong as the weak nuclear force. They suggest that in some instances, it may even counteract the effects of gravity. (Wilford, 1987)

In recent years, there have been two seismic cosmological discoveries that have dramatically increased the attention scientists have been giving to the idea of a fifth force. The first of these discoveries was that most of the mass in the universe is composed of an unknown form of matter. We touched on this in the previous chapter: dark matter. Quite a few physicists are convinced that not only does dark matter consist of undiscovered subatomic particles, it could ultimately be a part of how the fifth force works. (Chown, 2011)

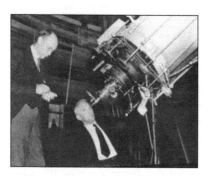

Figure 4.3 *(Source: Astronomy.com, 2020, license unknown)* Vesto Slipher (bottom) accompanied by Carl Lampland using the 24-inch Clark refractor, in this undated image.

The second discovery was that the universe seems to be expanding at an accelerating pace. This discovery actually took place at the beginning of the 1900s. Astronomer Vesto Slipher suggested that galaxies seemed to be receding from the Earth based on his study of the light they gave off. (Slipher, 1913). Not long after, using Einstein's field equations, Russian physicist Alexander Friedmann presented his own evidence suggesting universal expansion. (Friedmann, 1922) It wasn't until 1924, however, that Knut Lundmark from Sweden provided the first observable evidence. His work was so accurate that his calculations were only 1% off from the best measurements we have today! (Steer, 2012) Ever since then, we've been trying to understand this cosmic expansion. Some refer to the force making this expansion possible as dark energy, or 'quintessence'. (Wetterich, date unknown; Cicoli, 2012)

Dark matter and dark energy form the most common basis for building an explanation and framework for a fifth force. They're the most logical starting point for building a new theory of physics, and they are the most accepted by the mainstream scientific community as well, with most physicists, astronomers, and mathematicians in agreement that they exist—even if we can't yet fully explain them. We can detect the anomalies they present, but we're still having trouble measuring them.

And that's arguably the biggest problem we face right now, and why experimentation has been somewhat limited (but growing!). Take the gravitational force, for example. Even though we have a fairly robust understanding of how gravity operates, it actually requires very sensitive equipment and instruments to measure it, because it's a rather weak force unless you're analyzing very large objects with sizeable mass. As I mentioned earlier, many scientists believe that the fifth force is likely similar in strength to gravity, or perhaps just slightly stronger, and that means that we need equally sensitive equipment and instruments to properly recognize, identify, and measure how it works.

Hungarian physicist Loránd Eötvös carried out his famous Eötvös Experiment in the late 1800s, and built upon it through the early 1900s, demonstrating that inertial mass and gravitational mass were seemingly the same. (Fishbach, 1986) This work would lead to the development of the equivalence principle in Einstein's theory of general relativity.

But fast forward eighty years: a team of particle theorists in the 1980s reassessed Eötvös' work and they found that this classic, bedrock test of the equivalence principle "hinted that all was not well with Newtonian gravity." (Schwarzschild, 1988) Simply put, we still have a lot to learn about gravitational force.

As I've said before, for the purposes of this book, there's no real need to get too technical, but understanding the equivalence principle does help us to understand how a fifth force would and likely does operate. Take a look at Figure 4.4.

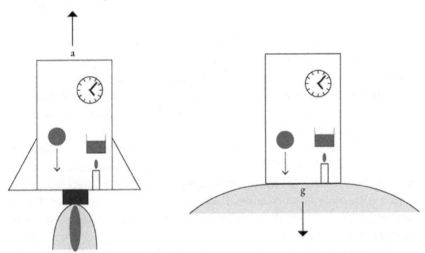

Figure 4.4 The principle of equivalence states that there is no physical difference between an accelerating frame of reference and one in a gravitational field. If the two frames are equivalent, then gravity can have special effects, such as bending light.

Essentially, the principle says that gravitational and inertial (or accelerative) forces are similar and usually hard to tell apart. For example, if a windowless laboratory was stationary on the Earth's surface, being held there in place by gravitational force, and a second laboratory of identical design was on a spaceship travelling at an inertial speed opposite but equal to the gravitational force, the scientists inside the moving laboratory would be unaware that their laboratory was moving. There would be no physical difference between the two frames of experience. (Schombert, 2015) Time would pass the same. Gravity would work the same. The other fundamental laws of physics would operate the same.

Testing the equivalence principle is one-way physicists are searching for a fifth force. A fifth force would not be bound by the equivalence principle. I'll outline an example for you. Take the way light travels and the way its rays can be bent. The equivalence principle tells us that all things being equal, light should travel and bend the same everywhere in the universe because it is bound by the rules that govern gravitational and inertial forces. But as you'll recall from Chapter 3, we looked at two instances where an unexplained bending of light has been observed.

The first instance was Dr. Mellier's analysis of dark matter using the telescope in Mauna Kea, Hawaii. His team's observations suggested gravitational effects that were strong enough to bend light. Similar light-gravity distortions were observed by Maurice Allais when his instruments were thrown off during solar eclipses.

Another way to search for the presence of a fifth force is by studying the gravitational force at extremely tiny scales in order to observe deviations. One of the first attempts to carry out this analysis was called Project SEE (Satellite Energy Exchange), an international effort "to develop a space-based mission for precise measurements of gravitation." (Sanders, 2000) Its researchers identified gravity as "the missing link in unification theory" and noted that finding a potential violation in the laws of gravity was the most important aspect of the project because it could mean the existence of new particles or energy at work.

While Project SEE seeks to establish proof of gravitational violations in space, physicists have also been finding violations down here on Earth. In the 1980s, a team of Australian geophysicists believed they stumbled upon a fifth force at work when they were measuring the gravitational constant in extremely deep mine shafts. (Schwarzschild, 1988) The gravitational calculations they predicted didn't line up with what they actually measured during their experiments. The measured values were 2% short of their predictions. The conclusion of their research was that a low-range repulsive force counteracting gravity must be throwing off the gravitational constant. An unexplained force was altering gravity!

Figure 4.5 (*U.S. Navy, photo by Journalist Seaman Joseph Caballero, license unknown*) The USS Dolphin in the San Diego harbor.

The United States Navy discovered similar gravitational anomalies using an unusual submarine called the USS Dolphin, which was built specifically to "test new technologies and equipment at ocean depths of 3,000 feet." (Dougherty, 2020) Among a long list of missions, naval scientists used the Dolphin's extreme depth capabilities to evaluate fifth force potential. In a report issued by the Department of the Navy, Commander Wayne Peterson explained several of the submarine's missions in 1989. It was titled 'Newton's Inverse Square Law of Gravity' and its objective was to test the strength of Earth's gravity. "Recent experiments in both laboratories and mines suggests that the earth's gravitational field may increase with depth. If this can be proven to be true the fundamental law of physics may require modification." (Department of the Navy, 1990)

Finally, in Greenland, while testing gravitational force in boreholes drilled into the ice sheets, the same discrepancies between the predicted measurements and the actual recorded measurements were observed— off by a few percent. (Ander, 1989; Zumberge, 1990)

Beyond gravitational force anomalies, other forms of research find equally exciting proof of a fifth force. The Japanese Belle Experiment which ran from 1999 to 2010 detected excess nuclear particle decay caused by new particle formation. (Moskowitz, 2015) Hungarian scientists analyzing nuclear decay in the hopes of discovering dark photons (dark energy) discovered excess decay rates as well, suggesting the presence of some unknown energy at work. The experiment went even further though: the excess energy actually formed a new subatomic particle. They called it the X17 particle, and it is believed to be a 'force carrier' for the fifth force. (Cartlidge, 2016; Cockburn, 2019)

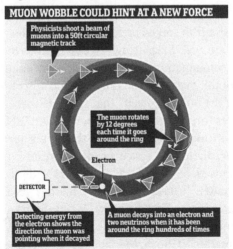

Figure 4.6 (*Source: unknown, license unknown*)
Faster particle wobble suggests an unknown force at work.

In 2021, scientists at the Fermi National Accelerator Laboratory outside Chicago announced they had found deviations in measurements of charged muons (elementary particles similar to electrons). The particles wobbled at a faster rate than they should have. They believe that new, unexplained subatomic particles are at work, enabling an unknown force. The Science and Technology Facilities Council in the U.K. said the Fermi experiment "provides strong evidence" of a new force. A researcher at the University of Manchester said the findings point "to a future with new laws of physics", and Professor Ben Allanach at Cambridge University said the evidence got his Spidey sense tingling, adding, "I have been looking all my career for forces and particles beyond what we know already, and this is it. This is the moment that I have been waiting for and I'm not getting a lot of sleep because I'm too excited." (Ghosh, April 2021) A similar experiment took place in Switzerland using the famous Large Hadron Collider at CERN. While smashing subatomic particles together, they found an excess of electron formation. (Ghosh, March 2021)

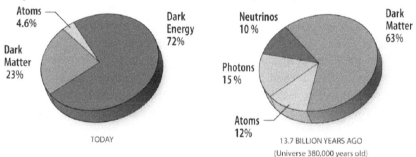

Figure 4.7 *(Source: NASA, WMAP data)*
Measurements of the Wilkinson Microwave Anisotropy Probe's data results.

We know that a fifth force is real because we know that dark matter and dark energy are real. Measuring the cosmic microwave background (the leftover electromagnetic radiation from the Big Bang), physicists have calculated that all the matter in the universe accounts for just 30% of the critical density of the universe itself. That suggests that an unknown form of energy accounts for the other 70%. (Spergal, 2007) NASA's Wilkinson Microwave Anisotropy Probe, a satellite that spent ten years recording electromagnetic radiation in space produced results that estimate the universe is composed of 72% dark energy, 23% dark matter, and just 4.6% ordinary matter. Just 4.6% ordinary matter! As the University of Bristol's Dr. Konstantinos Petridis says, "We do not know what 95% of the Universe is made of or why there is such a large imbalance between matter and anti-matter." (Ghosh, March 2021) This is one of the dynamics of the fifth force that make it so frustrating, but also so exciting. It's in the absence of knowledge that we know the fifth force is real.

Earlier, I mentioned *quintessence*, the nickname for the unknown dark energy force that is causing the accelerating expansion of the universe. Here too, we find another way in which the fifth force is proven to be real. The initial experiments in the late 1980s by Ratra and Peebles, which were the starting point of the study of quintessence, suggested that this dark energy form was 'time-varying'. (Ratra, 1988) In other words, unlike the cosmological constant, which was Einstein's proposed static rate of universal expansion and does not change, quintessence is dynamic—it changes over time. (Wanjek, no date) What makes this so interesting to me is that it can be either an *attractive* force or a *repulsive* one, depending on the ratio of its kinetic energy, which scientists can't quite explain yet. I believe this fits into the yin and yang model of subtle energy or Qi. If quintessence can exert itself so dynamically, it would explain the unique polarity characteristics of subtle energy. Attraction and repulsion. Yin and yang.

ORIGINS: ANCIENT WISDOM

In a slight departure from the science, and to close out this segment of the chapter, I'd love to point out the origins of the word *quintessence*, as well. I think you'll find it quite interesting, and it demonstrates something I've always believed: that looking to the past to understand the world around us and where we're headed in the future is one of the most valuable and instructive processes we can undertake.

Figure 4.8 *(Source: unknown, license unknown)* Traditional representation of the five classical elements. The dodecahedron signifies the Universe, or aether.

The term quintessence comes from the Latin, *quinta essentia*, or *fifth* element. Ancient civilizations like the Greeks believed in a core set of so-called classical elements. You've probably heard of these before: water, earth, air, and fire. Based on the ideas of his mentor Plato, Aristotle believed there was a fifth element, which he called the *first element*. The classical four were considered terrestrial, or of the Earth. The fifth/first element, however, was considered celestial, or of the Heavens or cosmos. Soon, this first element was given a name: *aether*. Aether was believed to move in constant circles, in the most natural way, and it was this perfect motion that Aristotle used to explain the orbits of stars and planets. (Lloyd, 1968; Smoot III, no date)

I find it fascinating how the fifth classical element shares eerily similar attributes to the modern fifth force. It is yet another in a long line of correlations between modern scientific discovery and ancient knowledge and wisdom that rippled through the civilizations before us. The concept of the quinta essentia was not just of its time. In the Middle Ages, many philosophers built on the concept. They believed that aether could shift in density, but was generally an extremely thin and spread-out element which filled the universe. Medieval cosmologist and mathematician Robert Fludd referred to aether as "subtler than light," a conclusion that developed upon the views of Hellenistic philosopher Plotinus, who said the element was both penetrative (everywhere) and non-material (invisible). (Fludd, 1659) Hmm... sounds like the fifth force to me!

It is said that Isaac Newton himself used the concept of aether to conceive his early electromagnetic and gravitational force theories, matching his observations to the rules of mechanical physics. (Osler, 2010) And even Albert Einstein admitted that when he was considering the physical properties of the empty space between matter, what would become his theory of general relativity, his calculations represented a sort of updated and mathematical variation on the concept of aether from the past. (Einstein, 1920) It's no wonder then, that when it became clear that dark matter and dark energy were real, and that they account for up to 95% of the content of the universe, we returned to the concept of the quinta essentia: the fifth element, the fifth force. They say history repeats itself. Perhaps it does. Perhaps, like aether, it moves in perfect circles, finding itself over and over again, causing new interactions of attraction and repulsion in a sort of balance and harmony. Subtle energy itself, hard at work, just out of reach of our ability to fully understand and explain it. But we're closing in fast, and it's becoming harder and harder to ignore what's all around us—energy.

VIBRATION, FREQUENCY, AND ENERGY

For me, the most exciting thing about this new frontier of science is that it feels like everyday people are finally starting to wake up as well. We're finally able to expand our minds beyond the rigid textbook standard theories and accept inventive, creative approaches to how we interact with our minds, bodies, and spirits. It may seem like I've been building a case for the large-scale, big-picture scientific breakthroughs, and to some extent I have, but by demonstrating how these universal truths operate, it becomes so much easier to bring it back down to Earth. All the shortcomings we looked at in Chapter 3, and all the exciting advances I've shared with you thus far in this chapter, have all shared something in common. This book, and the science it presents, is really about energy when all is said and done. This is a story of subtle energy, of Qi.

As scientists continue to explore new paths and build more and more evidence to support a new scientific revolution, we can't forget that healers and energy masters from ancient times through to today have harnessed the truths of this revolution, even if they haven't been able to explain it in mathematical calculations or theories of physics.

With the body of evidence we do have, both past and present, we know that subtle energy is real. Whether you call it Qi or Prana, dark energy or the fifth force, the wording and names don't really matter that much. What we know for sure is that this force operates as energy: resonant frequency. Vibration. It's wavelengths and signals.

If you've followed any of my work before, or if you've used my devices, you know that frequency is the key to unlocking everything. We exist in fields of energy at every point along our journey in this life. Learning how to navigate and manipulate those fields, to adjust and balance them, to tap in and out of them as needed... That's the answer. That's the real secret to a balanced life in harmony.

Figure 4.9 *(Source: unknown, license unknown)*
A visual representation of the Akashic Record.

I'm reminded of the beautiful Hindu notion that the universe keeps a sort of database of everything that has ever happened across the cosmos by encoding vibrational patterns on distant matter throughout the universal expanse. A sort of fingerprint of time and space. They call this the 'Akashic Record'. According to tradition, it is possible to access this cosmic database. Think of it as an intergalactic library where you can access all the information of the universe. The focussed individual can tune in to the record's vibrational patterns—like finding the right frequency on a radio tuner. (Swanson, 2003) *Akasha* or *akash* is the Sanskrit word for 'sky' or 'aether' in Indian cosmology. The word finds its origins in the root word *kāś*, which means 'to be'. For Vedantic Hindus, akasha is one of the Panchamahabhuta, their version of the classical elements. It is the fifth element and is considered to be singular of its kind, an eternal and all-pervading substance that is imperceptible. (Potter, 1977; Iannone, 2001) Indian Jainists have an even more complex breakdown of akasha. They believe it operates through sentient beings and souls, non-sentient matter, the principle of motion, the principle of rest, and the principle of time. (Balbir, 2010) And what almost all Indian traditions share is their belief that akasha's main characteristic is the attribute of sound. (Muller, 2003) And what is sound? Ah, yes: frequency.

By tuning our dials accordingly, we can tap into the universal frequencies. We can hear them. We can feel them. We can transmit them. We can receive them. Every elemental particle operates by spinning or vibrating. *We* are made of elemental particles. To me, this is an exhilarating and profound realization, and it is one that many scientists grapple with as well. One of the supreme questions of both traditional scientific models and of those that are shaping this new frontier of science is this:

What is the fundamental substance of the universe: matter or energy?

MATERIALISM (MATTER) VS. VITALISM (ENERGY)

Beyond the concepts of physics, biology, and chemistry (the so-called hard sciences), there is also a philosophical debate that rages on about the make-up of the universe. On the one side, there is *materialism* (sometimes called *physicalism*) which argues that matter is the fundamental substance of the universe. Materialists believe that all things, including consciousness itself, are the result of material interactions (physical substances engaging with one another). On the other side is vitalism, which argues that consciousness (or energy) is supreme, and that matter and physical interactions are the result of that energized consciousness. In other words, matter and material objects only exist because the energy of our consciousness perceives them and wills them to be. Without the energy of consciousness, there is nothing. (Novack, 1979; Edwards, 1967) I suppose you could look at this philosophical debate from the perspective of the old expression: *which came first—the chicken or the egg?*

Exploring these two philosophical dynamics is a good exercise for the mind, and a valuable way to understand just how critical energy is—not only as a basis for our existence and how we experience the world, but also as a basis for how we can change the world around us and our place within it. In essence, both philosophical views attempt to answer what reality is made of, how it came to be, and where it comes from.

Let's start with materialism (physicalism). Materialists believe that the primary building block of the universe is matter, and that mind, spirit, and consciousness (energy) are secondary. Put more simply, mind, spirit and consciousness only exist because matter exists. (Novack, 1979) Materialists argue amongst themselves about what exactly *matter* is. (Herbermann, 1913) Some of that argument looks like this:

- Is there a single type of matter, or are there multiple types?
- Is matter a continuous substance that expresses itself in multiple forms, or is it a collection of separate unchanging substances?
- Does matter have intrinsic properties or not?

When Einstein developed his general theory of relativity, the question of what matter is became somewhat more complicated because his theory proposed that matter and energy are essentially interchangeable, which would mean that matter could be subject to energy in certain instances. As the Standard Model of particle physics and quantum field theory built upon Einstein's research, materialists generally held to their original position, however, that matter is supreme and energy is a product of matter. Put in scientific terms, matter is *prima materia*: it comes first. But this position is difficult to maintain as we find out more and more about the universe.

We know now that the overwhelming majority of the universe is composed of unknown or dark energy, but scientists remain unable to explain what that energy is. (Sadoulet, 2007) Even in this cloud of doubt and uncertainty though, most scientists agree that the definition of matter has changed. As German physicist Werner Heisenberg noted, materialism rested upon the belief that matter could be explained perfectly down to the atoms of things. "This extrapolation, however, is impossible... atoms are not things." (Heisenberg, 1962) The famous philosopher Noam Chomsky comes to a similar conclusion: it's not good enough to just say something is matter. "Anything can be considered material," if one decides it is. (Chomsky, 2000) He essentially argues that we have to dig deeper.

And this is where many reject the concept of materialism altogether, particularly when trying to describe or understand the concept of consciousness, ideas, human functioning, etcetera. Matter simply doesn't explain everything in a complete or comprehensive way. Rudolph Peirls, one of the physicists who worked on the Manhattan Project (which produced the first nuclear weapons), said, "The premise that you can describe in terms of physics the whole function of a human being ... including knowledge and consciousness, is untenable. There is still something missing." Nobel laureate Eugene Wigner agrees: materialism is "not logically consistent with present quantum physics." (The Economic Times, 2012) If something is missing then, what is it? That's where vitalism comes in…

Vitalists believe that the fundamental building block of the universe is energy (spirit, mind, consciousness), and that matter is secondary. (Novack, 1979) Nobel-winning physicist Erwin Schröedinger was among those who argued that consciousness simply can't be accounted for in physical terms. He proposed that consciousness was absolutely fundamental. (Schröedinger, 1984) Energy is the building block for everything else.

Old-school vitalism relies on concepts of a *vital spark* or *life force*, essentially the aether that we looked at earlier in this chapter. (Williams, 2003) Modern vitalism builds on those ideas, taking into account new scientific discoveries in the last few decades. Many modern physicists point out that "a shadowy and paradoxical conjunction of waves and particles" exists as vibrations of invisible energy form the foundation of the universe. (Davies, Gribbin, 1991) Nothing would exist if it weren't for vital energy forces dominating the cosmic landscape.

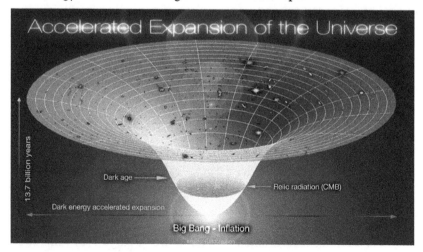

Figure 4.10 (*Source: Coldcreation, design by Alex Mittlemann, license unknown*)
A visual representation of the Lambda-CDM model.

This philosophy is backed up by what is known as the Lambda-CDM (cold dark matter) model. This cosmological model suggests that the universe contains three major components: Dark energy, dark matter, and ordinary matter. It attempts to explain the energy forces at work causing the expansion of the universe, accounting for quintessence—the fifth element, while working within the boundaries of general relativity. In the most simple terms, it says that dark energy is the predominant building block of the universe and admits that we can't quite explain what exactly that energy is, how it works, or where it comes from. (Kroupa et al, 2010)

As always, ancient civilizations and beliefs were ahead of their time, and support our new understandings of the universe through this vitalist lens. In Buddhism, we can find much knowledge to support this perspective that energy comes first. Dharmakīrti, a philosopher from the 6th or 7th century, wrote that consciousness experiences itself and nothing else. Everything we perceive as objects (all matter) is just consciousness (energy) expressing itself. (Kapstein, 2014) From this, I believe we can interpret that energy is the building block. It's the starting point. It allows for everything else… and because of this, if we can tap into it, we can alter our own reality. We can evolve ourselves. We can improve ourselves. We can heal ourselves. And where do we tap into this superhuman ability? In the vacuum…

THE VACUUM AND ZERO-POINT ENERGY

What is the vacuum, you ask? Well, if you're a science fiction buff, or if you watch a lot of movies about aliens, the vacuum is something way out in space, somewhere where nothing can exist. But scientifically speaking, the vacuum is all around us, even down here on Earth. In essence, it is the space between particles. It even exists inside atoms themselves as the space between electrons and the nucleus! So, by one definition, the vacuum is basically the absence of matter, but it could also be defined as a sort of *universal matter*. (Swanson, 2010) Put another way, it is dark energy, or just… energy itself.

Scientists believe the energy in the vacuum is enormous. They also believe that it fluctuates greatly. This limitless, constantly changing energy is called 'zero-point energy'. (McTaggart, 2001) Imagine yourself standing outside. Around you are particles that form the air. We take the air for granted most of the time. It is essential for us to breathe it, but in most cases, it has no effect or consequence on the way we go about our lives. But when the billions of atoms that make up the air are energized and begin to move in an organized, collective motion (like wind), we are forced to acknowledge its presence. The same phenomenon exists for life forms in water. Under normal circumstances, sea creatures exist unaffected by the water around them, but when the particles that make up the water move in a current, wave, etcetera, they are forced to maneuver and respond accordingly. This is, in a simple sense, how the energy in the vacuum works. And when we speak scientifically, we usually call these collective vacuum forces electromagnetic or gravitational fields.

Figure 4.11 *(Source: Swanson, 2010)* Fish don't usually perceive the water around them, just like us humans don't usually perceive the air around us, but we are both affected by these invisible forces that surround us when the particles that make them up move in concert at the same time, in the same direction.

In the vacuum, these invisible fields of energy can operate in complex ways and exist in complex states. From everything we can gather, it seems irrefutable that subtle energy is one of these complex states. In fact, it would appear as though zero-point energy is essentially just subtle energy itself, operating in various ways to create various effects. It is generally imperceptible, but when it acts in concerted motion, it makes itself readily apparent. We don't yet fully have the evidence or vocabulary to explain how this all works, but from observational data, and by analyzing the spaces where there is an absence of matter or energy, we can come to some very solid conclusions.

Many experiments have begun the work of explaining how vacuum states can emerge. Take the work of Gariaev and Poponin. Using a vacuum chamber, they shined a light on DNA samples, illuminating them. The light altered the state of the vacuum, creating particles that were both invisible and massless. These particles remained in the vacuum even after the DNA samples were removed from the chamber. These *phantom* particles formed energy patterns. This provided evidence that new vacuum states can be created. (Gariaev, 1992; Poponin, 2002) The laws of physics as we know them can't explain this. It is something entirely new to us—instant energy.

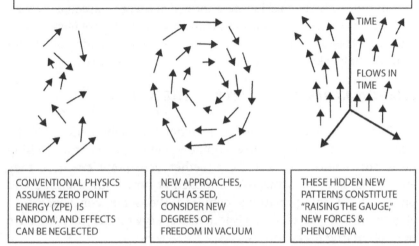

THE VACUUM ZERO POINT ENERGY MAY HAVE MANY DEGREES OF FREEDOM NOT INCLUDED IN CONVENTIONAL PHYSICS (GARIAEV, 2002; TILLER, 2001′ LOZYREV, 1958)

CONVENTIONAL PHYSICS ASSUMES ZERO POINT ENERGY (ZPE) IS RANDOM, AND EFFECTS CAN BE NEGLECTED	NEW APPROACHES, SUCH AS SED, CONSIDER NEW DEGREES OF FREEDOM IN VACUUM	THESE HIDDEN NEW PATTERNS CONSTITUTE "RAISING THE GAUGE," NEW FORCES & PHENOMENA

Figure 4.12 *(Source: Swanson, 2010, license unknown)* The energy in the vacuum is usually thought to be random in movement, but it often arranges itself in consistent patterns and alignments, similar to how the particles of air and water form wind and currents, vortexes, turbulence, etcetera.

It has been shown that vacuum energy can be reshaped, re-formed, and reconstituted. Conventional science is just now coming to terms with how this functions. As Claude Swanson describes, "The vacuum resembles a dynamic liquid which can flow in many patterns, including forward and backward in time. The extra modes of motion are types of subtle energy." (Swanson, 2010) Mainstream science must accept that these anomalies are the rule and not the exception. They are the blueprint of the universe and if we accept this reality, we can begin to truly understand how everything works in a connected fashion. Vacuum energy doesn't just pop out of nowhere, even if it may appear that way at times. It isn't unpredictable, random, or chaotic—it just follows laws we simply can't describe yet. Indeed, it is emitted by all particles in the universe, and as a result, it is connected to all other particles. This is the cosmic web I have mentioned so many times before. It is a network: the superhighway on which energy travels through the cosmos. If we ask the right questions and look in the right places, we can merge onto this highway and use it to our advantage.

This is the secret which is now revealing itself more clearly as we move forward in the scientific revolution. It is how energy healers are able to project energy nearly instantaneously, even across great distances. They are tapping into the 'information field', the underlying universal fabric of space and time. They're actively travelling on the energy superhighway. They are tapped into the zero-point energy of the vacuum. (Swanson, 2003, 2010) They are exercising the fifth force, manifesting it, and transmitting it. Their consciousness, formed of energy, can actually create changes in the vacuum. (Swanson, 2003) This is the future of physics. This is the new frontier. Science has never been in a more exciting place, and we're still only taking baby steps. There's so much more to learn!

CHAPTER IN REVIEW: REALITY OF THE WORLD

In this chapter, we've pieced together how subtle energy is the building block of the universe, and how science is just now catching up to this reality. The fifth force, aether, zero-point energy... they are all one and the same. We've looked at how both scientific and philosophical interpretations come to the same conclusions, in alignment with the ancient wisdom and energy mastery that we have been observing for centuries.

Subtle energy is the link and the bridge between conventional scientific understanding and the seemingly paranormal, supernatural, and unexplained phenomena that present themselves constantly across cultures, civilizations, and time. It is the answer to all our biggest questions. As we develop a stronger grasp of it, it will unlock the universe to us, but more than that, it will allow us to unlock ourselves, to hack our reality. This is what the word 'biohacking' means, and why you're hearing it used so much more these days. (We'll talk about that more later...)

In these last few chapters, I have attempted to build a framework of knowledge for you so that you can understand *what* subtle energy is, as well as the basics of *how* it works. We've even looked into the feats of some of the world's greatest energy masters. You now have a fairly stable and expansive comprehension of the fundamentals. In the next chapter, I will take a greater leap. We will explore what subtle energy can *do* when it is *applied*—beyond just the energy healing of the masters.

I will dive into government-funded experiments, communication breakthroughs in telepathy and ESP, subtle energy's effects on the natural world, and much more. We'll look at how subtle energy has the ability to completely reimagine how we interact with the universe. I'm confident that these exciting subjects will blow your mind—just like they continue to blow mine. The new frontier is waiting for us.

If you believe that energy is the fundamental building block of the universe, or if this book is starting to prove to you that it is… then you might just be a vitalist. Spirit, mind, consciousness. Tapping into the zero-point energy of the universe. That's the vitalist way. You, too, can live out a life shaped by Qi.

Living a vitalist lifestyle, or Qi Life, requires a relaxed, balanced, grounded body and mind. But most of us do not enjoy this kind of energy stability. We often feel fatigued or in pain, like our bodies aren't working optimally. Qi deficiencies can have tangible effects on our emotional well-being as well—feelings of depression, anxiety, irritability, etcetera. All of this can be reversed by balancing your Qi.

- Protect your body from sickness and disease
- Increase your endurance and clarity
- Improve your state of mind
- Ignite your inner fire

My team and I have developed carefully-tuned frequencies to achieve all this and more. And there's no better device to put these frequencies to use than our powerful Qi Coil™ lineup.

>>> **Visit www.GetQiCoils.com to get your Qi Coil™ System and transform yourself 1% a day.**

SCAN ME!

CHAPTER 5

BECOMING SUPERHUMAN

What does the word 'superhuman' mean to you? Perhaps it conjures images of superheroes with flowy capes and superpowers. Maybe it reminds you of your childhood and all the crazy ideas your imagination could come up with. Do you envision bulging muscles and feats of adrenaline—a mother lifting a car to save her child, or a giant bodybuilder lifting five times his weight in a strength competition? Or maybe your version of superhuman is something a little more grounded in reality: a single parent who can do it all, a firefighter who rescues a dog from a burning building, a journalist who reveals mass corruption, an everyday hero who foils a criminal's plans or helps an elderly person across the street…

There are many ways to be superhuman. Some of them seem challenging. Some seem impossible, even fictional. And I bet most of them seem exceptional, as though being superhuman is out of reach. It can often feel like only a special few possess the strength, stamina, courage, intellectual capacity, or wherewithal to live up to the word. And what about you? Do you feel superhuman? Would you like to?

In this chapter, I'm going to take you on a journey of superhuman abilities. We'll look at some of the unbelievable ways that human beings can live out their superhuman powers. I will paint a picture of a world that seems far-fetched and out of reach, but if you've been paying attention to this book so far, you know that everything I'm sharing here in these pages is rooted in objective truth and evidence. That means the people and experiments I'm about to share with you are all real. And more than that, they share a common denominator: subtle energy.

Every one of the people you're about to read about is accessing energy forces that already exist within and around them. They have simply discovered, or been taught, how to tap in to those energy fields, to use that energy to accomplish the extraordinary. They've learned how to control and channel the flow of Qi, and in so doing, they have essentially evolved. That's the endgame of the scientific revolution I've been telling you about: personal evolution. It's the next step for humanity. No longer accessible just to the few who have mastered it, but readily available for all who seek new levels of growth, to level up their lives.

Limits can be transcended. Human potential can be unlocked. That's the power of Qi, of subtle energy. The resonant frequencies of the universe are available to all… no capes required, no origin stories needed. Just you and *your* intentions. Are you ready to meet some superhumans?

LOOKING BACK… SEEING FORWARD

Before I take you through some of the more recently observed examples of superhuman abilities, let's take a quick journey through time to reflect on some of the instances recorded in the pages of history.

Ancient China was one of the most fertile grounds for early superhuman accounts, and it's no surprise why. The Chinese have a long history of accepting extra-sensory powers as legitimate abilities, without the stigma or biases that other cultures engage in. In *Romance of the Three Kingdoms*, a 14th century historical novel that details the real-life events that transpired during the end of the Han dynasty between 169 AD and 280 AD, many superhuman figures are accounted for.

One of these figures is Zhuge Liang, a statesman and military strategist whose intellect in warcraft has been compared to Sun Tzu, the writer of *The Art of War*. (Nojonen, 2009) Zhuge Liang spent much of his youth studying astronomy and the role of energy in both day-to-day and military strategies. (Clear Harmony, 2005) Two of the battles that Zhuge Liang was involved in are recorded as having involved feats of superhuman ability. In the Battle of Yiling, it is said that upon arriving along the Yangtze River at Yufu Shore, general Lu Xun felt a strong enemy presence. He sent his men to scout further ahead and they reported back that a strange arrangement of stones in a maze-life formation was blocking their way forward. Lu Xun suspected the stones to be the work of Zhuge Liang but assumed they were merely a deceptive obstruction. Foolishly, he led his men inside the maze. A strong gust of wind emerged, causing a dust storm that blocked out the sky. The stones forming the maze began closing in on the soldiers. When all hope seemed lost, an old man emerged and led Lu Xun and his surviving men out of the maze. He told Lu Xun that Zhuge Liang had predicted that a Wu general would pass through the area, and had constructed the maze as a trap. The maze was built on the Bagua principle, a series of symbols that represent the fundamental elements of reality—part of the Tai Chi and Wuxing philosophies which account for yin and yang, as well as the five phases (cosmic agents of change). (Yu, 2000)

In the buildup to the Battle of Red Cliffs, a fire attack on warlord Cao Cao's fleet is about to be deployed. General Zhou Yu realizes with horror that the wind is blowing in the wrong direction for the attack to be successful. As the winds are, they would cause the blaze to backtrack onto his own men. Zhuge Liang promises that he can change the direction of the wind in Zhou Yu's favor and performs a ritual for three days and three nights. On the third night, the winds shift and the attack on Cao Cao's fleet is successful. Such tales of Zhuge Liang's clairvoyance and psychokinesis are well documented in *Romance of the Three Kingdoms* and in other ancient works. His prowess in military strategy is tied to his ability to psychically read his adversaries' thoughts and foresee future events in ways that sound like remote viewing, which we'll look at shortly. These abilities would grant him the nickname 'Crouching Dragon', always at the ready to attack.

Abilities like these were held by others in the era as well. General Guan Yu is another documented example. Revered after his death as a god of war and benevolence by Confucianists, Taoists, and Buddhists alike, Guan Yu was said to be unstoppable, often exhibiting superhuman strength and stamina as he willed events to his desires. (Perkins, 1999) It is for this reason that many believe he had a mastery of his Qi energy, perhaps to the point of being able to manifest, an ability we'll look into in the next chapter. For the purposes of this chapter, however, several examples of Guan Yu's superhuman abilities come to mind. The first was his legendary journey across five mountain passes, during which time he slew six generals. At one point on this quest, he is obstructed by general Han Fu and 1,000 soldiers. Han Fu manages to hit Guan Yu with an arrow. To the amazement of the soldiers, Guan Yu pulls the arrow out of his arm, seemingly unfazed, and charges toward Han Fu, killing him. The soldiers are so shocked that they allow Guan Yu to pass. Interestingly, this is not the only time Guan Yu suffers an injury to the arm. In the Battle of Fancheng, his arm is struck by a crossbow bolt coated in poison. After the battle, he is attended to by doctor Hua Tuo, who says he must cut open the arm to scrape the poison from the bone. The doctor offers to secure the arm in place to avoid flailing from the pain, but Guan Yu famously declines. The surgery is carried out with Guan Yu showing no sign of pain, all the while using his other hand to play a round of weiqi, an ancient board game. This level of mastery over the body's physical matter, to completely suppress pain receptivity, showcases truly superhuman mental ability, the ability to create an alternate cognitive reality.

And speaking of Hua Tuo, no reference to *Romance of the Three Kingdoms* would be complete without mentioning the extra-sensory powers of this mystical physician. Hua Tuo was considered several hundred years ahead of his time medically speaking, perhaps the first doctor to use anesthesia. (Mair, 1994) His courtesy name (a sort of nickname often given in East Asian cultures) was Yuanhua, which translates to 'primal transformation'. (Chen, 2007) He was known for maintaining his youthful appearance for his whole life, often referred to as a 'xian'. Xian is the Daoist term for a being believed to be immortal, transcendent, or celestial. Hua Tuo was said to practice Daoyin, a form of Daoist neigong, which is a meditative process that cultivates, directs, and refines Qi energy. Daoyin is considered to be the historical precursor to the practice of Qigong. (Huang, 1987) Hua Tuo was known to use acupuncture and moxibustion as part of his diagnosis and healing strategies, both of which are means to regulate the flow of Qi. His healing powers were considered legendary and it was believed that by assessing his patients' Qi flow, he could see the illnesses inside them.

Another branch of legendary, historical superhumans includes the so-called *blind warriors*... In the 14th century Japan, we find famous long-swordsman and combat trainer, Toda Seigen. He began to slowly lose his eyesight, so he started training himself in short-sword combat so that he could continue to fight in close proximity, where his senses were sharper. (Rogers, 1990) Legend has it that he was undefeated in combat as a blind man, seemingly unvexed by his lack of vision. He was apparently able to decipher where his opponent was, and even what their next move against him would be. This legend seems to be one of the origins for such modern superheroes like Daredevil: the refinement of extra-sensory perception. Another famous blind superhuman was the 12th century King of Bohemia, John the Blind. He rode into battlefields on horseback, killing many enemies, despite his vision setbacks. As the legends go, he would say before battle, "Take me to the place where the noise of the battle is the loudest. The Lord will be with us." (Franciscus, 1784) And of course, perhaps the most written about blind warrior, Goliath, who infamously took on David in Biblical record. Historians now believe Goliath "suffered from visual field restriction as a result of acromegaly," but was able to overcome this by tapping into his other senses in battle after battle... until he met David, of course. (Berginer, 2006) Figures like these are generally perceived to be legendary or mythical, but did they have superhuman abilities working in their favor? Is it possible they were tapped into a frequency or wavelength that allowed them to carry out feats of extraordinary, extra-sensory ability? Could they see, without seeing?

REMOTE VIEWING

"Using the standards applied to any other area of science, it is concluded that psychic functioning has been well established." These are the words of Dr. Jessica Utts, a member of a remote viewing panel established by the CIA to review the validity of the agency's infamous Stargate Project. (Utts, 1996)

Let's start with some basic definitions. 'Remote viewing' is the ability to sense impressions of distant subjects or events without direct contact or even prior awareness. It can be performed in real-time or in advance of events yet to happen. (Blom, 2009) When it is carried out before something occurs, it is referred to as 'precognition'. (Swanson, 2003) Those who can engage in remote viewing often describe the process as accessing an 'inner eye' through a sort of out-of-body experience. (Guiley, 1991) It is said that in order to facilitate clear impressions, the practitioner must pay attention to their imagination, let go of any preconceived judgment, and develop a relaxed state. When the subject or event of the viewing session is locked onto in the mind, it is referred to as the 'signal line'—like tapping into a frequency. The U.S. intelligence community considers less than 1% of the population capable of remote viewing, with some experts saying it's as low as 0.2%. (Swanson, 2003) But if given the right training, resources, and encouraged to shed societal and cultural skepticism, might that number be much, much higher?

Figure 5.1 *(Swanson, 2003, photo by Dr. Harold Puthoff, license unknown)* CIA scientist Dr. Richard Kennett, remote viewer Pat Price, and Dr. Hal Puthoff, pioneers of 1970s remote viewing research.

The study of remote viewing, or *clairvoyance* as it was known then, began in the mid-nineteenth century with researchers like the well-known electrochemist Michael Faraday, whose early work in electromagnetism changed the face of science as we know it. (Hyman, 1985) Research and experiments carried on sporadically over the decades, with initial U.S. Defense Department and CIA studies starting in the early 1950s according to declassified documents. (Mandelbaum, 2000) Things really intensified in the 1960s and 70s as governments and intelligence agencies began funneling massive amounts of money into studying the phenomenon. These included Soviet Military and Soviet Secret Police initiatives carried out across more than twenty laboratories in the Soviet Union. Soviet physicists were so convinced of the power of remote viewing that they suggested it was "enmeshed with all of everyday life" and that ordinary individuals held "vast, hidden potential" to tap into these superhuman powers. (Ostrander, 1970) Government-funded studies were a dime a dozen in the heat of the Cold War as the United States and the Soviet Union raced to develop any edge they could over the other. In a 1972 Defense Intelligence Report that was declassified decades later, it was said that "the powers of the subconscious mind are vastly superior to those of normal consciousness." (LaMothe, 1972) One Major General went as far as to say, "If you didn't believe that remote viewing was real, you hadn't done your homework." (Schnabel, 1997) Wide-reaching efforts were made to recruit individuals already in the armed forces who possessed or demonstrated enhanced psychological abilities, or who had described experiencing vivid near-death experiences. (Swanson, 2003)

One such individual was Pat Price, a California businessman, who would prove to be one of the all-time great remote viewers. After teaming up with the Stanford Research Institute (SRI), and under the study of researchers Hal Puthoff and Russell Targ, Price famously provided impressions of a secret Russian weapons facility that the CIA didn't even know existed! He provided detailed descriptions of the site and the activities being carried out there, sketching out his visions on paper in the process.

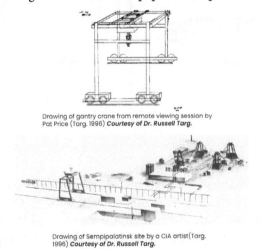

Drawing of gantry crane from remote viewing session by Pat Price (Targ, 1996) *Courtesy of Dr. Russell Targ.*

Drawing of Sempipalatinsk site by a CIA artist(Targ. 1996) *Courtesy of Dr. Russell Targ.*

Figure 5.2 *(Swanson, 2003, sketches by Pat Price released by Dr. Russell Targ, license unknown)* Price's sketches of a secret Russian military site.

When the CIA was presented with Price's remote visions, they had no idea what to do with the information and were unable to precisely locate or identify the location, but four years later, Price's visions were proven to be almost entirely accurate. The site was being used by the Soviets to build anti-ballistic missile weaponry, and its discovery was the precursor to President Reagan's 'Star Wars' program. (Swanson, 2003; Targ, 1996)

In another one of Price's remote viewing sessions, he was able to accurately identify and describe classified rooms inside multiple embassies targeted by U.S. intelligence. He explored the buildings in his mind and was able to identify interior design aspects, the locations of doorways, and much more. A CIA operations officer attached to the viewing session concluded that after careful consideration of the results, he believed that remote viewing, "whatever it is," offered the agency unique operational abilities. (Swanson, 2003; Mandelbaum, 2000)

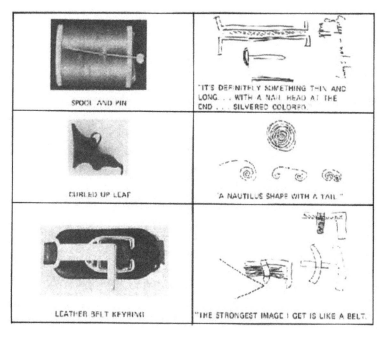

Figure 5.3 *(Swanson, 2003, sourced from Puthoff, 1981)* Examples of target objects for remote viewers beside the sketches of the items they made, correctly identifying the targets without having seen them.

Generally speaking, a remote viewer is provided with or comes up with their own, 'target'—something to lock onto in their mind from a distant place or time. The Stanford Research Institute frequently challenged remote viewing subjects during their 1970s experiments by providing concealed target objects, which the viewers were then tasked with describing. These could be simple objects like spools, leaves, or keyrings. The viewers would then draw what they believed the concealed objects were. Many viewers not only described the objects correctly but could describe some details with millimeter accuracy. (Puthoff, 1981)

Despite massive evidence for the legitimacy of remote viewing as a psychic practice, but also as a weaponizable skill, governments and mainstream scientists would later wash their hands of the ability. Even the larger research efforts like the Stargate Project were eventually closed out and dismissed. Some experts, including talented remote viewer Joe McMoneagle, have argued that the politicians overseeing projects like Stargate were simply not believers in the paranormal and that even some of the project directors were "afraid of the paranormal." Many leading figures began to grow embarrassed to be associated with the study of something so weird and unconventional. McMoneagle knows a thing or two about remote viewing; he was one of the most accurate military viewers, with a reported 65% accuracy rate. (Swanson, 2003; McMoneagle, 1999)

The Princeton PEAR Lab carried out over three-hundred-and-thirty-four experiments on remote viewing under doctors Robert Jahn and Brenda Dunne in an attempt to gather statistical certainty one way or the other that the practice was valid. Their analysis confirmed that a real 'signal' was being tapped into by the studies' subjects and that the accuracy of the subjects' visions being down to chance odds was small: one in fifty-five billion to be exact. (Swanson, 2003) These findings were replicated more than seventy times by researchers all over the globe. (Radin, 1997)

What makes remote viewing so incredible is that it genuinely breaks the rules of science as we know them. Jahn makes a point to clarify that the 'signal' that remote viewers tap into does not seem to weaken over great distances, and it seems able to function outside the boundaries of time. This means this energy force is stronger than electromagnetic or gravitational forces, which both weaken over distance. (Jahn, 1987) "It's as if consciousness is somehow able to direct its influence directly across space and time, an understanding that certainly poses a challenge for science." (Jahn, 1992) Based on the data, time travel itself may or may not be possible, but mind travel across time absolutely is. This means the number of *paths* into the future is potentially limitless. If a remote viewer can detect what lies ahead, they can alter the course of their actions or those of others. Imagine the possibilities this could have on manifesting and shaping one's own future! "It seems that the consciousness can easily move in space and in time." (Swanson, 2003)

It is hypothesized that the average person's remote viewing powers exist predominantly in their dreams. Take Nobel Prize-winning physicist Niels Bohr. He devised the model of the atom that we rely on today, which he claims came to him in a dream in the early 1920s. A Bell Telephone engineer during World War II dreamed of a radar-guided anti-aircraft system. When he woke up, he drew out the schematics feverishly, and just a few years later, the system was being used in combat. (Swanson, 2003; Rheingold, 2000)

Remote viewing is finding wider popularity across industries and fields of research. In China, medical applications are on the rise. Government-sponsored research is showing that certain viewers can detect illness and disease in patients, even with just a few minutes in the patients' presence. One such viewer, a young boy, was able to accurately diagnose ninety-three out of one-hundred-and-five patients! (Dong, 1984) Business and financial uses have also been documented. Gerald O'Donnell has famously used remote viewing to predict stock market trends. He even teaches other investors how to tap into the 'signal' for themselves. (Swanson, 2003) The use-cases for remote viewing are truly far-reaching and arguably limitless.

What does all this teach us? Chiefly, remote viewing demonstrates that consciousness is not a finite resource. It doesn't stop with the boundaries of our body. It is more universal. It is energy. It can be tapped into. This amazing ability also forces us to reassess our understanding of what time is… If a remote viewer can see events before they occur, or retroactively without having been there themselves, then time isn't linear. It must be a sort of archive that can be flipped through forwards and backwards— remember the Akashic Record? If remote viewing is made possible by the fifth force we've been discussing in this book, then it may prove to be a true sixth sense. Maybe we're all capable of extra-sensory powers. We've just been lacking the imagination to explore them, or been too afraid to admit that our consciousness is more interconnected with the universe than we like to think it is. Just how *extra-sensory* can we be?

EXTRA-SENSORY PERCEPTION (ESP) AND TELEPATHY

While remote viewing is the visual-based ability to see events or subjects at remote locations, extra-sensory perception (ESP) is a broader means of information gathering. Remote viewing is typically seen as a trained or controlled process and skill. ESP, by contrast, is a more pervasive, constant form of psychic ability. In short, ESP is the ability to receive and transmit information using only the mind. This exchange of information is often referred to as 'telepathy' and does not involve the known human senses or any physical interaction. (Carroll, 2005)

Modern scientific research into this psychic ability finds its roots in the late 1800s, with Duke University's J.B. Rhine building up to his prominent experiments in the 1930s. He and his wife created the popular

Zener cards, a series of cards featuring symbols and shapes. In the experiments, a 'sender' attempts to transmit the imagery on a card to a 'receiver'. (Sladek, 1974). This sort of experiment remained a tried-and-true method of testing simple thought transference for decades. On the return trip from the moon aboard the Apollo 14 mission, Captain Edgar Mitchell, the sixth man to walk on the lunar surface, pulled out some paper with photographs of a deck of cards on it. He had pre-arranged several 'receivers' back on Earth without telling anyone and concentrated on the cards in an attempt to transmit the data back home using only his mind. Two of the four receivers correctly identified fifty-one out of two-hundred cards. The odds of this happening by chance were one in three-thousand! (Mitchel, 1971; Clark, 1973)

The Soviets also tested ESP in space. Their cosmonauts were specially trained and reportedly able to "communicate telepathically more easily with each other than with people on earth." (LaMothe, 1972)

Like remote viewing, whatever energy form or signal allows ESP to function appears to violate the laws of physics, and does not weaken, even over great distances. The U.S. Defense Intelligence Agency's declassified reports on the subject, in agreement with Soviet findings, suggest that ESP functions better in space than on the surface of the Earth. Claude Swanson points out that this may be due to the lack of bombardment from man-made electromagnetic fields from all of our electronic equipment, cables, satellites, etcetera. (Swanson, 2003)

The evidence for ESP has been constantly building on itself for decades. In the 1940s alone, over three million trials using more than forty-five hundred participants were carried out. Since then, the number of trials has surpassed nine-hundred-thousand! As Dean Radin concluded, "These experiments did cause many scientists to take psi phenomena seriously." (Rosenthal, 1978; Radin, 1997)

In 1957, the chairman of the Psychology Department at the University of London affirmed the findings that had amounted to that time. He said the only conclusion that a reasonable person could come to, in the face of the evidence at hand, was that a sizeable percentage of the population is able to "obtain knowledge existing either in other people's minds, or in the outer world, by means as yet unknown to science." (Eysenck, 1957) Sixty-five years later, we still aren't 100% sure what those 'means as yet unknown' are, but it seems almost certain that those means are, in fact, subtle energy: the fifth force. Practitioners of ESP, like those of remote viewing, are simply tapping into the resonant frequencies of the universe.

The Chinese refer to those capable of such powers of the mind as "exceptional human functioning". China is one of the few countries whose government is still openly recruiting psychologically adept people through public, well-funded programs. One program conducted in the early 1980s was focussed on finding exceptional children. Many kids were discovered to have strong ESP capabilities. One young girl, in particular, was tested by multiple universities and government and military laboratories. In one experiment, she was asked to describe a drawing sealed inside a lead box designed to contain radioactive materials. Within twenty minutes, she had the drawing in mind, virtually to exact detail. (Swanson, 2003; Dong, 1984)

Interestingly, ESP is not just a feat of humanity. Animals have been found to demonstrate similar psychological powers. Dr. Rupert Sheldrake famously studied dogs' abilities to know when their owners are coming home—not the time they usually walk in the door, but the time when the owner *decides* to return home. His research between 1997 and 2000 confirmed that dogs share a psychic connection with their owners. (Sheldrake, 1999) It's not unusual to hear people describing their pets as having a sort of *sixth sense.*

A sixth sense is something we recognize in ourselves as well. The feeling of déja vu is a good example. Another is when we find ourselves thinking of someone, and then that person reaches out or comes into our lives somehow. We tend to ignore these instances as coincidence, happenstance, or just gut feelings because we have no other way of making sense of them, but we sell ourselves short in doing so. What we are brushing off is actually a cosmic connection of universal information. We are *tuning in* to the subtle energy that surrounds us at every moment. The question is: *are we listening?*

Just how do we go about locking onto the signals of universal Qi? One method that scientists have discovered is through hypnosis. Several studies have documented increased ESP accuracy when we are in an altered state of consciousness, like when hypnotized. One such study went on for thirty-seven years and found a notable increase in abilities among the test subjects analyzed. (Stanford, 1994) Meditation is another way to enhance ESP experiences. Both methods quiet down the mind, relaxing our state of consciousness and making us more receptive to the energy fields around us. Likewise, both hypnotized and meditative states can be achieved artificially when the body is subjected to specific frequencies which induce relaxing brain wave patterns. (Swanson, 2003) This is something my team and I have focussed on when developing our devices, which I'll talk more about in a later chapter.

Sensory deprivation or electromagnetic noise filtering is a powerful way to tap into subtle energy fields. This may be why sensory deprivation pods have become so popular in recent years at spas around the world.

When we cut ourselves off from the world around us temporarily, we are able to heighten our senses, including our sixth sense.

Figure 5.4 *(Swanson, 2003, photo by Carol Sabick and Skip Atwater of the Monroe Institute, license unknown)* The doorway to the Monroe Institute's special isolation room.

One laboratory, in particular, has made this sort of cognitive blockade a central focus of their ESP research. The Monroe Institute in Virginia constructed a special isolation room which blocks out electromagnetic and sound waves, allowing a person inside to reach otherwise impossible states of deep relaxation. When inside, subjects exhibit changes in the resistance (or elasticity) of their skin (i.e. even their skin relaxes), as well as changes in the voltage that their bodies emit. (Swanson, 2003) These sorts of measurable bodily reactions are a critical component in the research that supports ESP abilities.

We know, for example, that when someone is receiving information by ESP, their blood volume increases. Their brain waves and heart rates also fluctuate. (Dean, 1966) We can even detect a clear distinction between the left and right sides of brain activity during ESP transmission. The left brain, known for its order, verbal, and analytical function actually interferes with ESP. When under hypnosis or in meditation, the practitioner is effectively quieting this side of the brain, allowing information to be processed subconsciously. We can see this in real-time when analyzing EEG (electroencephalogram) scans, which monitor brain activity. (Swanson, 2003; Pavlova, 1967)

The research seems to be very conclusive that ESP abilities are far wider-spread than we typically account for, but our consciousness, which is biased and burdened by interference, cultural notions, and general disbelief in the paranormal, supersedes our subconscious, which appears ready and willing to lock onto the cosmic signals and frequencies available to it.

As usual, ancient civilizations (and those that continue to exist more or less unbothered by the modern world) have been proven well-tuned to these subconscious energy fields. Explorer Douchan Gersi spent time with the remote Tuareg peoples of Northern Africa and reported many examples of extra-sensory abilities including ESP, telepathy, and even energy healing. Many of the Tuareg were particularly adept at isolating timing through ESP—when certain events would happen, for example. (Gersi, 1991)

Time and space appear to share quite a strong intersection with ESP, as it happens. Research suggests that ESP is more accurate at certain times of the day and on certain parts of the planet. James Spottiswood of the Cognitive Sciences Laboratory in California reviewed thousands of paranormal functioning studies and discovered that one's position on the Earth relative to the stars in the sky made a dramatic difference in the accuracy of ESP abilities. This relation between position and stars is referred to by astronomers as 'sidereal time'. (Swanson, 2003; Spottiswood, 1997)

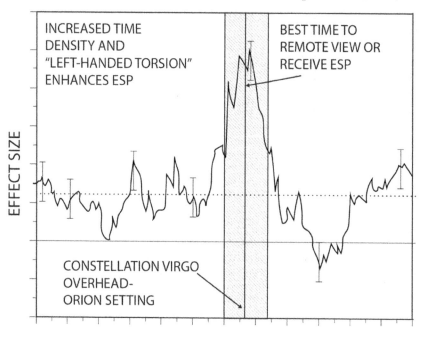

LOCAL SIDEREAL TIME (HOURS)

Figure 5.5 *(Swanson, 2003, diagram by Dr. James Spottiswood, license unknown)*
Peak ESP reception at 13.5 hours sidereal.

In his results, Spottiswood noticed that extra-sensory ability was strongest when the constellation Virgo was above the practitioner. This section of the sky is at 13.5 hours sidereal and "is known as the 'Great Attractor' because it is a huge concentration of 'dark matter'". (Swanson 2003) In fact, this section of the sky has an intense pull of gravitational energy and is in the direction that our galaxy is being pulled toward as the universe continues to expand. This connection between dark matter and gravitational pull likely correlates with strong left-handed torsion energy, which we discussed earlier in Chapter 3. The compounding accuracy of extra-sensory powers during this sidereal time (day or night) is a whopping fourfold! (Swanson, 2003; Spottiswood, 1997)

All of this analysis, in combination with that on remote viewing earlier, exhaustively proves that extra-sensory abilities are not only real but accessible to us all... if we know where, how, and when to seek them out. The human consciousness is capable of tapping into universal knowledge and information, unobstructed by time and space. When we allow our mind to connect with these cosmic frequencies, we can see places, things, and events—in past, present, and future tense.

But our capacity to *access* this information (to receive and transmit it) is entirely different from our capacity to *exert* this information. How we *use* these abilities to *affect* the world around us is a leap even further into becoming truly superhuman. Prayer, visualization, intention, manifestation... Changing the physical world by bending it to our will and desire.

PSYCHOKINESIS AND TELEPORTATION

Being superhuman is about more than just having powers. It's about using them to enact changes in the world around us. 'Psychokinesis' (or *telekinesis*) is the mental ability to influence the physical world without any physical interaction. (Xiong, 2010) More simply, it is the power to affect objects or beings from a distance, often without touching them. Quite literally, mind over matter.

One of the most studied practitioners of psychokinesis was Ingo Swann. In 1972, one of the first laboratory-tested experiments he took part in occurred at the Stanford Research Institute, under the review of physicists Hal Puthoff and Russel Targ, whose other work in this field we covered earlier. Underneath the SRI building was a specially crafted superconducting magnetometer, designed to measure magnetic fields. The device was used to look for quarks, one of the elementary particles, and due to this very precise use, it is heavily shielded from all possible external wavelengths and frequencies. Magnetic shielding, aluminum,

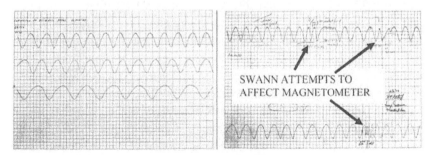

Figure 5.6 *(Swanson, 2003, graphs provided to Swanson by Dr. Harold Puthoff, license unknown)* Wavelength interruptions caused by Ingo Swann's psychokinetic powers.

copper, supercooled niobium... the device was protected by layer after layer of impermeable materials. Previous SRI testing had yielded no signals from the outside world in the magnetometer's data sets. (Swanson, 2003; Puthoff, 1974)

Puthoff and Targ explained to Swann how the device's inner detector functions: it generates a magnetic field, which weakens over time. The field's strength is recorded as wavelengths on an output graph. As the field weakens, the wavelength starts to elongate and flatten out. Swann indicated he would focus his attention on the inner detector. As he did so, the frequency of the wavelengths doubled. Puthoff and Targ's output graphs recorded the exact moment this happened, as seen in the figures here. On the left, the normal weakening of the wavelength. On the right, the moments when Swann's subtle energy exertion affected the device. (Swanson, 2003)

One of the ways this experiment can be explained is by the concept of the 'astral body'. The astral body is an element of our consciousness which can travel beyond the boundaries of our physical body. Some people refer to this as a component of the out-of-body experience (OBE), or as part of the 'subtle body'—part of the human consciousness that is neither fully physical nor spiritual. The concept is an important part of traditional Taoism, Hinduism, Jainism, and Buddhism, among others, with the earliest known ancient mentions found in 2nd century BCE Taoist texts. (Samuel, 2013) Modern science has only just begun to explore the concept, particularly in the research of meditation (Loizzo, 2016), but recent findings have proven quite astounding. "When the subject sets his intention, his consciousness immediately seems to go to the place of interest." Swanson, 2003) Dutch scientists have weighed the human body of subjects before, during, and after experiencing an OBE. On average, the subjects studied experienced a weight loss of 2 ¼ ounces during their OBE. (Mitchell, 1987; Carrington, 1975) The astral body, therefore, is actually measurable; it has a weight! Detectable physical attributes like this, though seemingly invisible to us, demonstrate that intentioned subtle energy moves within the physical world. This phenomenon also helps explain remote viewing. The astral body travels from the body to the target location, allowing the viewer to see something their body is not physically present to see. Returning underground at the SRI in 1972 then, it seems as though Ingo Swann's astral body was able to go *inside* the magnetometer and physically affect its inner detector.

Affecting a device by invisible means, though technically a physical interaction, is still quite hard to visualize. That's where more in-your-face examples come in handy. Uri Geller was a well-known psychokinetic during the 1970s. Friends with presidents, scientists, and television

Figure 5.7 (Source: unknown, license unknown)
A young Uri Geller with a bent fork, knife, and spoon.

personalities, he was most famous for bending spoons. Dr. Werner Von Braun, a rocket scientist who helped develop advanced missile systems, and Nobel Prize-winning physicist Brian Josephson of Cambridge University, were both believers in Geller's superhuman abilities. Von Braun said there was no known scientific explanation for what Geller was capable of, and Josephson confirmed that his experiences with Geller proved that psychic abilities were real. Stanford's Materials Science Department studied many of the spoons that Geller had bent under electron microscopes. Their conclusion was that the metal in the bends of the cutlery appeared visually distinct, appearing to have been melted at high temperature. (Tiller, 1992)

Another example of an amazing superhuman was Nina Kulagina, a Soviet woman who was studied extensively in the 1960s. She was famous in the Soviet Union and beyond for many superhuman psychokinetic abilities, such as moving objects using only her mind. During some tests, she was able to move objects weighing as much as one pound! (Gris, 1978) Most of the objects she was tasked with moving were non-magnetic, eliminating the possibility that she was using some sort of hidden magnet to carry out her feats. (Swanson, 2003) A particular skill of hers that was tested frequently was her ability to develop camera film simply by thinking about it or looking at it. She was even able to create patterns and shapes on the film as it developed by moving her eyes accordingly. (Sergeyev, 1972) Perhaps her most amazing psychokinetic feat was causing a gap or split in a confined cloud of smoke. During many of the experiments featuring Kulagina, her body was connected to physiological, electromagnetic, and brain wave monitoring systems. When exerting psychokinetic energy, she frequently generated unexplainable electrical pulses, creating a measurable energy field around her. (Rejdak, 1968; Kolodny, 1968; Kurz, 1968; Sergeyev, 1967, 1968) Kulagina is arguably one of the most studied psychokinetics ever, with research into her abilities going as high up in the Soviet Union as the Theoretical Physics Department at Moscow University. Her powers proved a strong correlation between the mind and electromagnetism, one of the four fundamental forces we reviewed in Chapter 4. But she was observed to create electric fields up to 10,000 volts per centimeter (Ullman, 1973), which suggests that that correlation goes far beyond the fundamental. Indeed, it requires the acknowledgement of a different force entirely—a fifth force. Subtle energy.

Electrical measurements are one of the most commonly used metrics in psychokinetic research. Qigong masters and energy healers have been studied in this way, as their ability to affect the physical nature of the body by projecting their subtle energy is, of course, a form of psychokinesis. As you'll recall from Chapter 2, the Menninger Clinic in Texas, one of the top-ranked psychiatric hospitals in the United States, attached electrodes to the earlobes of energy healers, and the results demonstrated inexplicably high voltage readings. Under normal circumstances, a human being emits between 0.010 and 0.015 volts, but Qigong masters and energy healers measured between thirty and three-hundred volts, ten-thousand times greater than usual! (Green, 1993)

One of the largest-scale examples of subtle energy emission and its electromagnetic correlation is the apparent lightning control abilities of Ted Owens. On the night of May 10, 1967, in Philadelphia, Owens asked his friend, attorney Sidney Margulies, to pick a spot on the horizon. Margulies obliged, and moments later, lightning struck the spot he had chosen. Owens was known for carrying out weather-affecting psychokinetic feats like this with some frequency over the years, and his abilities were relatively well-documented. He came to be known as the 'PK Man', PK being short for psychokinesis. (Mishlove, 2000)

And finally, no conversation about moving objects with the mind would be complete without approaching the subject of teleportation, the transfer of energy or matter from one place to another without the physical traversing of the space between both points—instantaneous, faster-than-light positional transference. By any conceivable human law of physics, we have no way of explaining a phenomenon like this. But there have been some credible accounts of it through the years. Perhaps the most famous example from the 20th century is that of Captain Dubois, a French medical officer, whose visit to an Arab village caused an international stir. A villager by the name of Abdul reportedly made a photograph appear in Captain Dubois' hands… a photograph from his home in Paris. At the exact moment in Paris, someone in the home noticed the picture was missing, assumed it was stolen, and filed a police report shortly thereafter, claiming a break-in! Hours later, the villager sent the photo back to Paris. (Clark, 1973; Ayling, 1968)

No laboratory experiment has yet yielded something as miraculous as Captain Dubois' experience with his potentially superhuman villager friend, but prospects have been encouraging through a process called quantum entanglement. Essentially, a pair of particles (generally photons) are created in a state of entanglement. The particles are then sent in different directions. Regardless of distance, if we can detect the spin of one of the particles, we know the spin of the other, and this means we can deduce the material state of a particle over a great distance, which is an extremely important, but also very, very tiny piece of the teleportation puzzle. But you have to start somewhere! Experiments using this process of particle entanglement have taken place in Austria and Japan, among other places, and are seen as key to understanding how energy can enable matter to dematerialize in one place, and re-materialize in another without a loss of matter in-transfer. (Motoyoshi, 2000; Ritter, 1997)

Psychokinetic powers prove that subtle energy can flow from the human body (even from human consciousness) to external targets, affecting real-world physical interactions. Like so much of the research I've shared with you so far in this book, the examples of Ingo Swann, Uri Geller, and Nina Kulagina make it clear that we need a radical change of attitude and appreciation for these phenomena. Above all else, we need an open mindset within the scientific community, eager to explore that which can't be readily explained. And we must celebrate the researchers who dare to dive into that exploration, the true pioneers of this new frontier of science, this scientific revolution that we find ourselves at the threshold of. One example of this exploration is worth special mention…

RANDOM EVENT GENERATORS (REG)

At the PEAR Lab at Princeton University that I mentioned earlier, Robert Jahn and Brenda Dunne have directed some fascinating experiments—hundreds of thousands of them, in fact, over several decades! One of their studies involved a device called the 'random mechanical cascade'. Imagine a scientific version of the game Plinko from the game show *The Price is Right*. A small metal ball drops down from the top of the device and bounces around through a vertical series of pegs until it falls into one of the bins along the bottom of the device. Test subjects, most of them regular people with no known expertise in psychokinesis, were asked to manipulate the balls with their minds as they fell through the pegs. Other devices were used as well, including one that relies on the random noise of an electronic diode, emitting a random number of noise blips per second, and another device that detects radioactive decay from random source signals, emitting a random number of wavelength pulses per second. All of these devices are examples of random event generators (REG). Statistics and mathematics tell us that in the absence of interference, the balls, blips, and pulses of these devices will fall along the well-documented bell curve of random distribution, but Jahn and Dunne found entirely different results. (Swanson, 2003)

Test subjects, in most cases, were not physically near the REG devices. Most were not even on the PEAR Lab property, sometimes thousands of miles away. And to make the tests even more rigorous, the researchers had the subjects exert their psychokinetic energy at different times of day, sometimes even asking them to affect the devices at future times! On average, as shown in the graph here, when the test subjects were asked to increase the random distribution of the balls, blips, or pulses, they were able to, and likewise when asked to decrease the distribution. The probability of this happening by chance alone is just one in five-thousand. (Swanson, 2003; Jahn, 1987)

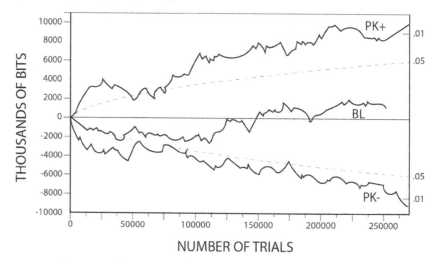

Figure 5.8 *(Jahn, 1987, as shared in Swanson, 2003, license unknown)*
Cumulative data gathered over a seven-year period at the PEAR Lab.

The accumulation of results over so many thousands of tests proves a statistical confidence that psychokinesis is real, that it can function independently of space and time, and that regular everyday individuals can exert its force using solely the power of their mind.

SUPERHUMAN SCHOOLS AND THE EASTERN EDGE – CHINA LEADS THE WAY

As I mentioned earlier, China has regularly been at the forefront of research into superhuman abilities. This is perhaps because their culture has a long history and tradition of recognizing the importance of subtle energy. For the Chinese, many phenomena that we in the West would consider paranormal are seen as simply *normal*. This greater openness and willingness to explore these abilities scientifically has often given them an advantage over Western research. In fact, it is not uncommon for entire organizations, university or military departments, and even schools, to be established to test, observe, and measure the subtle energy mastery of those they refer to as 'extra-high functioning'. Children are often the most sought after in this field of research, as it is believed that their minds, less biased by skepticism or doubt, are able to tap into unseen energy forces more easily.

Figure 5.9 *(Swanson, 2003; photo by Paul Dong, 1992, license unknown)* A young girl preparing to cause flowers to bloom on command before a panel of observers in Beijing.

One of the psychokinetic abilities that has been looked into by such establishments is the apparent ability to alter the rate of time. A specific example of this is the ability to expedite the growth of plants. Some subjects have been able to cause a closed bud to bloom (something that would have taken days or even weeks if left to occur naturally) from a rate of instantly to within just a few minutes. Some could make seeds sprout and grow within their hands. (Dong, 1997)

Other gifted children have been observed remote viewing, breaking twigs with their mind, adjusting watches from a distance, sensing others' thoughts, perceiving color by the sense of hearing, and much more. One girl named Yu Rui Hua could sense and identify hidden objects on a person's body, like the concealed gun of a security guard. Another little boy, Wei Ruoyang, could use his mind to sense where buried pipes were and describe their configuration, seemingly able to see through the dirt as if it weren't even there. (Dong, 1984)

A third-grade girl named Zhue Mei was well-known for her various mental abilities. She could move objects within sealed confines, like beans from a bottle, or unlock a padlock locked inside a box, both of which demonstrated a seeming ability to literally teleport objects through physical barriers. (Dong, 1984) Teleportation, naturally, defies every law of physics that we humans have devised, but China's extra-high functioning child subjects have repeatedly demonstrated the ability to disappear an object and make it reappear elsewhere, several tests of which took place under the supervision of the Institute of High Energy Physics and the Chinese military. (Hausdorf, 1998)

Another child named Zhang Baosheng was frequently called a national treasure in Chinese circles. He was once observed moving a bag of sugar weighing 100 pounds from one room to another. As he grew up, his powers seemed to become more precise and impressive. A high-ranking Chinese military official once asked that Zhang be locked inside a room, only to find the gifted young man at his house when he returned home that day. From then on, Zhang frequently worked with the Chinese Defense Ministry. Known for his heavy foot while driving, he would frequently get speeding tickets, but he was able to somehow make the paper record of the ticketing at the police station (this was before digital ticketing systems) disappear! In the late 1990s, it was reported that the Chinese military had a $20 million program in place to carry out ongoing research on him in order to keep up with his abilities as he aged. (Swanson, 2003; Dong, 1997)

Across China, and beyond, children are being trained to develop their superhuman, extra-sensory abilities. In the documentary *Superhuman: The Invisible Made Visible*, viewers are introduced to young children around the world, whose gifts are being developed rather than downplayed and suppressed. Many of these kids, like the blind warriors I touched on earlier, are being taught how to practice martial arts, archery, rollerblading, bike riding, and more, all while blindfolded. Some of them can even read without seeing the page. These techniques have been taught to children who are actually blind, as well, and they have experienced amazing results in their ability to function in a world without vision. Some schools even teach a process called 'vibravision,' the ability to see the vibrational energy of objects around you in order to perceive them without your eyes. Sounds like Daredevil's 'radar sense' or Spiderman's 'spidey sense', doesn't it? As one of the experts in the film says, "We exist as physical beings in an observable world, but our minds communicate in unseen ways with unseen forces." (Cory, 2020) At a fundamental level—at the level of our cells and DNA, we don't speak in language, we speak in energy.

Beyond the cultivation of young talent, China's (and its adjacent regional) history of superhuman legend is vast and deeply rooted. The Tibetans have a word that captures the energy force they tap into: *tummo*. It means 'inner fire'. Their specialized meditation form called gTum-mo is known to result in an increase in energy output. Harvard Medical School's Herbert Benson studied Tibetan monks between the 1960s and 80s. He believed their intense meditation could "uncover capacities that will help us to better treat illnesses." As he relayed from his research in the Himalayas, Buddhists do not consider the reality we live in as the ultimate one, that we can tap into universal truths that are not readily apparent to us in our normal existence. He observed monks performing radical and amazing feats, like spending entire nights sleeping in the snow at -17°C with only simple wool wraps on, returning to the monastery the next morning completely unharmed. He documented forms of meditation that could "help the mind control physical processes once thought to be uncontrollable," noting that the monks were able to adjust their body temperature, metabolism, heart and breath rates, and even their brain activity, seemingly on-demand. (Roa, 2017)

After spending so much time in the presence of these real-life superhumans, Benson said he hoped that their extra-sensory gifts would prove that self-care techniques can be on par with medical and surgical answers to health maintenance, upkeep, and healing. (Roa, 2017) And he's put in the laboratory work to show this is possible. He and his team once taught gTum-mo techniques to twenty-six test subjects unfamiliar with the meditation process. After just eight weeks of daily instruction on rhythmic breathing, chanting, and concentration, the subjects exhibited notable changes to their DNA. The "practice activated a set of genes used to make the body's cells more efficient at metabolizing energy." And that wasn't all. The subjects' telomere-protecting genes (telomeres are the part of our chromosomes that regulate our aging process) were also activated! (Devenish, 2013) Subtle energy, then, is clearly the secret to improved health and even longevity.

Another shining example of superhuman ability in the East can be found in Zhou Ting-Jue, a Qigong, Tai Chi, and Kung Fu Grand Master, as well as a Master Medical Qigong healer. Zhou Ting-Jue is renowned around the world. He began martial arts training and learning traditional Chinese medical theory with his uncle, who was a Taoist priest. You might have seen him on The History Channel's show *Stan Lee's Superhumans*. His practices have been studied by many, but few have replicated his abilities. Zhou Ting-Jue is known for his ability to intuitively sense where patients' pain and illness reside in the body, and to treat them therapeutically with his Qigong heat technique, a specialized form of energy healing. (Hill, 2010-2014) Through deep meditation and energy cultivation, masters like Zhou Ting-Jue have tapped into true mind-over-matter methods.

It would seem as though the West is sleeping on its ability to pursue advanced scientific inquiries into the incredible powers of the mind. The Chinese, and other Eastern cultures, take these powers and the energy forces that enable them, more seriously than we do. They are looking at ways to enhance these powers, to teach, train, and curate them in individuals, particularly children. Just as the West is falling behind China in areas like mathematics and the general hard sciences, so too are we losing our competitive advantage to understand how subtle energy works, how it can be leveraged, and how it can make us superhuman in the process. This unwillingness to take these matters more seriously is not only setting us back in terms of important, grand-scale endeavors like energy generation and military initiatives, but it also prevents us from working hand-in-hand with the Chinese and others to make leaps in more widespread applications like medicine, nutrition, mindfulness, and personal improvement. Superhuman abilities provide powerful insight into how we can harness subtle energy to improve the lives of all.

CHAPTER IN REVIEW

In this chapter, I hope you've come to appreciate the dynamism and variation of subtle energy applications. There are so many ways in which the fifth force can be channeled and applied. The examples of superhuman individuals we have gone through in these last few pages offer a glimpse into what each of us is capable of when our minds, bodies, and spirits are in sync. We can tap into unlimited cosmic energy, and the information it carries in its frequencies and signals.

The word 'paranormal' doesn't have to be scary or confusing. Broken down, it makes use of the ancient Greek *pará*, which means 'contrary to'. I would like to ask this: why should superhuman abilities, energy healing and mastery, or unexplained forces in the universe be considered *contrary* to the normal, or to universal principles? If these things are all happening in the universe, and the overwhelming evidence supports that they indeed *are* happening, then they aren't *contrary* to anything. In fact, by simply occurring and existing, these phenomena are a part of the universal theory of everything that science is meant to be in search of. To exclude them as distinct or *other* is simply the temporary product of our ignorance and shortcomings of imagination and discovery.

In the next chapter, I will explore a world where we take these phenomena for granted—as an accepted reality of the universal experience. If we are capable of bending reality with our minds through subtle energy, then infinite realities exist for each and every one of us. This concept of manifesting alternate personal timelines is often discussed under the umbrella topic of the 'multiverse'. I'll take you through what the multiverse is, and how the evidence suggests we can use it as a model to bring your desired reality into existence.

Want to bring out your own superhuman abilities? My team and I have been hard at work developing ways for you to harness your Qi energy and use it to transform yourself into a real-life superhero, in total control of your surroundings.

Our 30-Day Qigong Meditation Challenge focuses on four key disciplines of energy control:

1. *High-Level Martial Arts.* We explore how Qi plays a role in the concepts of offense and defense, just like it does in martial arts. This will open your mind to how best to position yourself in any situation.
2. *Energy Healing.* We take a deep dive into the oneness of mind, body, and spirit. Learning how to see the world through this lens will enable you to use Qi to heal yourself emotionally and physically, to find solutions to your problems, and to overcome obstacles. You'll gain the widest possible perspective of yourself.
3. *Manifestation.* Your greatest journey in life is your journey to success and security. Getting there requires the ability to foresee challenges and capitalize on the positive. Using Qi as a conduit to achieving your goals will change your perception of the possible.
4. *Psychic Ability.* By understanding how your personal energy field (biofield) works, and how to integrate it with the energy fields you come into contact with, you will be able to tap into deeper levels of consciousness, unlocking mind-bending abilities. Mind over matter through the power of Qi.

The 30-Day Challenge, in combination with our Qi Coils™, can accelerate your superhuman transformation. It's a true shortcut to taking control of your Qi—the ultimate training for energy harmonization. Become more powerful. Find your balance. And enhance your manifestation ability.

>>> **Visit _www.LearnSuperhuman.com_ to start your 30-Day Challenge.**

CHAPTER 6

THE MULTIVERSE: CONSCIOUSNESS, AURA, AND MANIFESTATION

M ost mainstream science considers the concept of the 'multiverse' to be hypothetical, but that shouldn't dissuade you from taking this exciting branch of physics research seriously. The Earth revolving around the Sun was once *hypothetical* as well, until it wasn't. As we've worked through this book, I've reminded you to keep an open mind. A worldview that allows for new information to be examined and contemplated is one that will always lead to a more well-rounded understanding of our world and the universe beyond. With that all said, consider the very serious scientific inquiry that the multiverse concept already enjoys. It's more than science fiction—it's science that can help us tell our own story, to manifest our desires.

So what is the multiverse? It's actually quite an expansive set of ideas, many of which compete with one another. At its core, it is simply the idea that multiple universes exist, that the one we find ourselves in is but one of many.

But it also depends on how you wish to approach the topic. We can talk about parallel universes, additional dimensions, alternate or parallel realities, levels of consciousness, multiple phases of cosmic frequencies, various planes of existence, the 'other side' or 'after life'... The list is actually quite endless, and since we are talking about something as gargantuan as the universe, it's not surprising that so many competing interpretations and theories exist. What's more, you can come at this topic from a purely scientific perspective, a purely spiritual one, or one that blends the two together in a sort of spiritual science. How you approach the subject is really up to which theoretical framework you place the most confidence in.

I am not here to tell you which approach is the most accurate, but what I can tell you with a level of high confidence is that we humans have been thinking about how our consciousness connects to the universe since our thoughts first became complex tens of thousands of years ago. The convergence of ancient and modern theories about what reality is presents some of the greatest evidence that subtle energy is real, and that it operates on more than one level or plane. Understanding this fluidity has allowed countless people through history to tap into something greater than themselves, and in so doing, to make themselves greater in the process.

In this chapter, I will explore some of the ways in which the multiverse has expressed itself historically through the lens of ancient wisdom, and empirically through the lens of modern scientific discovery. On the other side of this exploration, I'll move on to how an understanding of this concept, in conjunction with the understanding of subtle energy that we've been building chapter by chapter thus far, can allow you—yes, *you*—to shift your worldview in such a way that you will be able to navigate the multiverse, to use it as a means of personal transportation, self-discovery, and individual evolution. The multiverse is your portal to becoming superhuman. Let's begin...

ORIGINS OF MULTIVERSE THEORY

If we accept that a multiverse is essentially a group or collection of multiple universes, then we accept that within this group, literally *everything* is contained: information, matter, energy, time, space... and of course the laws, constants, and rules that describe and govern these things. What you may be surprised to hear is that this is not a particularly new idea or perspective.

Figure 6.1 *(Source: Wikipedia, creative commons)* Drawing of a marble bust of Lucretius (left), and photograph of a marble bust of Chrysippus (right)

The ancient Greeks were among the first to contemplate the possibility of multiple universes or realities using a philosophical framework known as 'Atomism'. Atomism proposed that everything in the universe is bound together by indivisible components called atoms, which exist within the *void*. (Berryman, 2008) This is actually how modern scientists chose the word *atom* to describe what we refer to as the smallest unit of physical matter today. To the Greeks, atoms were eternal, and as such, they were in constant motion and collision within the void. They believed that these collisions created endless parallel worlds less perfect than ours. These ideas would be played with and built upon for centuries. Third-century philosopher Chrysippus believed this eternal motion and collision of atoms and void meant that reality was in a perpetual state of expiration and regeneration and that this suggested that multiple universes had come and gone through time—a sort of cosmic recycling program if you will. Ancient Buddhist tradition would also come to a similar conclusion, suggesting that the world we know is just one of many, part of an infinite process of destruction and creation; this helps to explain their concept of reincarnation. Since we are made of the same eternal atoms as everything else in the universe, we too are recycled by way of reincarnation. (Sedacca, 2017) The ancient Romans were also frequent multiverse hypothesizers. Philosophers like Lucretius wrote of the idea in great detail in his well-known scientific poem, *On the Nature of Things.*

Fast-forward to medieval times, and European philosophers dipped their toes into the multiverse as well. In his 1255 work *De Luce*, English philosopher and scientist Robert Grosseteste contemplated that our world might be one of many. Durham University cosmologist Richard Brower has pointed out that Grosseteste believed the universe had "extra symmetry" that was beyond what we could comprehend. These ideas were so progressive, radical, and counter to standard Church opinion that Grosseteste was barred from writing more on the topic by the Pope himself. (Sedacca, 2017) After all, if *extra symmetry* meant the Earth wasn't the center of the universe—or that the universe wasn't the center of

Figure 6.2 *(Source: Wikipedia, public domain)* A 14th-century portrait of Grosseteste.

the universe (that there may even be more beyond or in tandem), then everything the Church stood for could be called into question.

But even papal decrees, like atoms in the void, come and go. And new collisions would arise in the 16th century. Italian mathematician and cosmological theorist Giordano Bruno was like many of the brave

Figure 6.3 *(Source: Wikipedia, public domain)* A bronze relief by Ettore Ferrari, showing the trial of Bruno by the Roman Inquisition. He was killed for his brave science.

scientists we've covered in this book. He wasn't afraid to break with the mainstream consensus. He famously suggested a plurality of worlds, that the Earth can't be the center of the universe because the universe has no center, that it is infinite. In that infinity, any number of worlds and suns was possible, and many of them likely mirrored ours: "an infinity of worlds of the same kind as our own," he wrote. (Singer, 1941; Sedacca, 2017) As mentioned in an earlier chapter, Bruno's bravery was ultimately his downfall. He was executed for his so-called radicalism.

Jumping forward to the 20th century, we can analyze the work of physicist Erwin Schrödinger, whose ideas we've touched on before. In the 1950s, he suggested the existence of multiple quantum states. When these multiple states are layered on top of one another, they form new, composite quantum states. This is known as 'superposition'. (Gribbin, 2012) Within the discussion of the multiverse, superposition would imply that other universes or realities aren't so much alternative, but rather, simultaneous. This approaches the concept of the multiverse in a more complex dynamic. Simultaneousness, of course, means that if there are other universes, realities, or dimensions, that they are parallel to our own and not just separate. They superimpose upon one another in a sort of mirrored infinity.

Recent research has added evidence to this notion of parallel-ness. In fact, it is research that we've already touched on in Chapter 4 in relation to dark matter/energy exploration in space. In 2010, the Wilkinson Microwave Anisotropy Probe's data encouraged scientists to consider that our universe may have collided with alternate, parallel universes at some

Figure 6.4 *(Source: Wikipedia, Creative Commons)*
Visual representation of the bubble multiverse.

distant point in the past. This evidence falls into modern physics fields such as string theory. As Tufts University physicist Alexander Vilenkin observes, "String theory admits an immense number of solutions describing bubble universes with diverse physical properties. The quantities we call constants of nature, such as the masses of elementary particles, Newton's gravitational constant, and so on, take different values in different bubble types. Now combine this with the theory of inflation. Each bubble type has a certain probability to form in the inflating space. So inevitably, an unlimited number of bubbles of all possible types will be formed in the course of eternal inflation." (Tegmark and Vilenkin, 2011) So we could be a world inside a galaxy inside a universe inside a bubble inside the multiverse. It's a lot to process!

As you can see, the scientific foundations of the multiverse have grown deeper and more complicated over the centuries. And that brings us full circle… German physicist Eckhard Rebhan is one of several recent researchers who has tied the concept of the multiverse to dark energy. He believes that the dark energy observable in our universe demonstrates that we are living in a 'sub-universe'—one of many parallel universes. This is an important connection between the multiverse and subtle energy. Rebhan suggests that dark energy is the connective tissue between universes. (Rebhan, 2017) And that falls in line with the *cosmic web* I've brought up time and time again. Subtle energy is the golden thread that connects every thing, every time, and every place in the cosmos.

The key then, as always, is to tread boldly in our new scientific revolution. As physicist Leonard Susskind says, "I would bet that at the turn of the 22nd century philosophers and physicists will look nostalgically at the present and recall a golden age in which the narrow provincial 20th century concept of the universe gave way to a bigger better multiverse of mind-boggling proportions." (Tegmark and Vilenkin, 2011)

VIBRATIONAL TRAP DOORS

As I outlined in Chapter 5, part of living a superhuman life has to do with control of the consciousness: mind over matter. We looked at many ordinary and several extraordinary superhumans and their abilities, and we've also discussed subtle energy masters and their amazing feats. One type of energy master we've only scraped the surface of is the yogi. Within the many religions of Indian culture, a yogi is someone who practices advanced yoga techniques while also incorporating deep, intense meditation. (Banerjea, 2014) Like most of the great energy masters across various cultures, both ancient and modern, meditation forms the root from which great powers blossom. Through this process of achieving higher consciousness, yogis are said to be able to tap into other levels of the physical universe. Yogis believe that the world we know is actually the lowest level in a much larger hierarchy of dimensions and that through enlightenment, one can actually learn to move freely from one dimension to the next. (Swanson, 2003)

They carry out this movement through psychic energy channels known as 'chakras', or cerebrospinal centers, which are seen as *trap doors* or exits through which the yogi can escape from the prison of the physical body and engage in other dimensions in spirit form. (Yogananda, 1946; Swanson, 2003) This separation of the body and spirit is a core component of many Indian traditions, and the two parts are often referred to as the 'subtle body' and the 'physical body'. (Sharma, 2006) Essentially, life as we know it exists in two basic dimensions: the physical, and the psychological. The subtle body is energy, while the physical body is mass. (Lochtefeld, 2002)

The well-practiced yogi makes use of the chakras, or trap doors, to have an out-of-body experience, where their consciousness is able to transcend time and space and engage instantly anywhere, in our dimension or others. Chakras are seen by yogis as higher-dimensional structures which enable access to subtle energy forms that our default state of consciousness simply doesn't have available to it. This is why the process of accessing this energy is considered an out-of-body or near-death experience, with both variations often called 'the other side'. Hindu tradition views this as the 'Astral realm' and accessing it is seen as 'crossing over'. (Swanson, 2003) I will circle back to what crossing over means later on, but for now, you will recall the astral body we spoke of in the last chapter. The astral body is the projection of consciousness outside the body. You can see how all these terms are interconnected and relate to the same phenomenon of interdimensional consciousness.

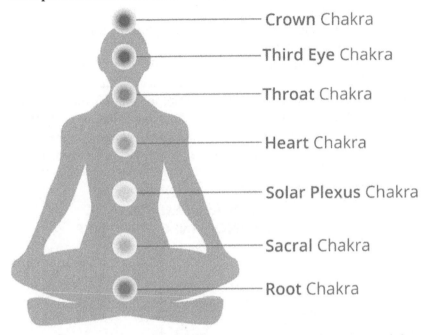

Crown Chakra

Third Eye Chakra

Throat Chakra

Heart Chakra

Solar Plexus Chakra

Sacral Chakra

Root Chakra

Figure 6.5 (*Source: Healthline, 2016, license unknown*) The seven chakras. The root chakra, or muladhara, is found at the base of the spine.

The root chakra, or muladhara, located at the base of the spine, is considered the most important of the cerebrospinal trap doors, as it grants the passer-through access to Kundalini energy. Like Prana and Qi, Kundalini is subtle energy, and it is one that is said to provide the ability to facilitate phenomena across dimensions or planes of existence. Only when the root chakra is energized with Kundalini can the other chakras come into alignment. Each of the chakras is said to rotate at its own unique frequency. Kundalini brings all of the frequencies into harmony and synchronization, creating a sensation of electric current running along the spine. (Frawley, 2009; Paulson, 1998) This current grows in strength as it emanates from the root chakra and flows to the next chakra, and the next after that, along its journey up the spine. Each chakra strengthens this current, resulting in a coiled flow. Scientifically speaking, this synchronization process appears to put the body into a coherent, macroscopic quantum state. Yogis say this is when the kundalini begins to flow in a truly free form. (Swanson, 2003) Studies have been carried out to support this...

In the early 1990s, Rosalyn Bruyere, a well-known energy healer, carried out research into the Kundalini experience with Dr. Valerie Hunt at the University of California Los Angeles. They wired yogis to electrodes as they went through their meditative process. What they found was that the electrode signals registered as white, which designates a full vibrational spectrum, suggesting an alignment of frequency as the Kundalini energy rose from the base of the spine. (Bruyere, 1994) These experiments uncovered something even more amazing: the yogis' bodies actually registered a shift in DC voltage. "All of the measurements were geared toward AC signals, which means they were looking for the vibrations in each chakra. But a DC shift means the *actual constant background voltage changed.*" Quantum mechanics explains a voltage change like this as the charged particles in the yogis' bodies changing their frequency. A sudden, overall shift in particle vibration in cosmological terms would be associated with an interdimensional shift. (Swanson, 2003)

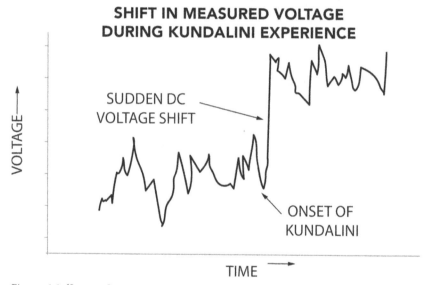

Figure 6.6 *(Source: Swanson, 2003; Bruyere, 1994, license unknown)* The sudden DC voltage shift in the body of a yogi going through a Kundalini experience.

This extraordinary synchronization of energy and consciousness is not exclusive to yogis, but it provides a specific snapshot of how one kind of subtle energy mastery enables it. Vibrational harmony is one of the keys to understanding how matter and energy intersect in a broader, universal way, and that's what we'll look at next.

THE SYNCHRONIZED UNIVERSE MODEL (SUM)

The physical nature of the world, the universe, and our default human experience within it, is made possible by an alignment of energy. When particles are charged in locked-in vibrational patterns, it is referred to as a 'phase state'. In simpler terms, particles are vibrating at a speed that we can perceive, but there are other particles, which vibrate at different speeds, which our senses, and even our instruments of measurement, are simply incapable of registering.

Figure 6.7 (*Source: unknown, license unknown*)
A dog whistle creates sound (frequency) that human ears cannot hear.

One way to imagine this is to think of a dog whistle. The frequency of a dog whistle is imperceptible to the human ear. This doesn't mean the frequency isn't there. It just means we can't perceive it. Now think much bigger. Think universally. We know that the majority of the universe is composed of dark matter and dark energy, but we can't perceive it directly. Instead, we know it's there because of the absences it creates and the seemingly paranormal phenomena it affects.

It is believed that this is how parallel or alternate universes or dimensions exist. They are composed of particles and energy which are simply not in alignment with our phase state. "Our reality describes only the matter which is synchronized with us." (Swanson, 2003) To experience a shift in vibration or frequency then, like yogis and other energy masters achieve, allows for the experience and perception of other phase states… or other realities.

This vibrational alignment, or synchronized particle system, is accounted for by the Synchronized Universe Model (SUM). Particles that are in vibrational sync can interact and exchange energy with one another, but particles that are not in vibrational sync cannot do so, and therefore, they are said to be in different phase states. They are *out of phase* with what we consider and observe to be the physical, material universe. (Swanson, 2010)

PARALLEL UNIVERSES
TWO SYSTEMS WITH DIFFERENT SYNCHRONIZATION CAN EXIST SIDE BY SIDE
AND BE UNAWARE OF EACH OTHER

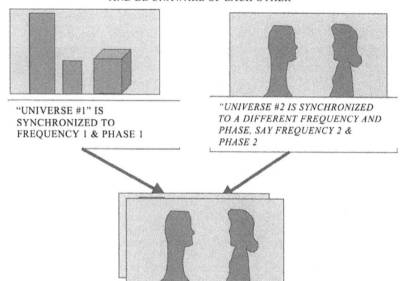

"UNIVERSE #1" IS
SYNCHRONIZED TO
FREQUENCY 1 & PHASE 1

"UNIVERSE #2 IS SYNCHRONIZED
TO A DIFFERENT FREQUENCY AND
PHASE, SAY FREQUENCY 2 &
PHASE 2

THE ELECTRONS IN UNIVERSE #1 ARE MOVING "OUT OF SYNCH" WITH THE
ELECTRONS IN UNIVERSE #2. THEREFORE THEY DO NOT "SEE" EACH
OTHER. THE TWO UNIVERSES CAN EXIST IN THE SAME SPACE AND TIME,
BUT "OUT OF PHASE." THEY ARE NOT AWARE OF EACH OTHER,
EXPERIENCE THE OTHER UNIVERSE ONLY AS "RANDOM NOISE".

Figure 6.8 *(Source: Swanson, 2003, license unknown)* Diagram showing how two distinct
phase states can merge, allowing for an overlap of experience between both states.

The multiverse then is simply a collection, hierarchy, or network of
distinct phase states. This means multiple or parallel realities or dimensions
can exist alternately or simultaneously in the same region of space-time
without mutual awareness of the other(s). The only hint that these other
phase states exist is what scientists call 'quantum noise'. Quantum noise is
essentially a measurable variation in small-scale particle vibration. It can
also be understood as a fluctuation in zero-point energy within the vacuum
we discussed earlier. It is a variance in energy that can't be explained. In a
synchronized phase state, we refer to the particle vibrations as coherent.
Quantum noise represents *decoherence.* (Clark, 2010; Townsend, 2012)

What little research we have to rely on at the moment suggests that
consciousness can interact between and across phase states, granting it
access to energy and information not found in our own phase state. In
other words, our consciousness can recognize and make sense of the
quantum noise. This can occur when the vibrational motion of matter
(its energy or frequency) in one phase state matches that of another.
(Swanson, 2003)

Dark energy, or subtle energy as we determine it to be, is the conduit or passageway between phase states. It allows us to see what is otherwise hidden from our senses and perceptibility. It is interdimensional.

LEVELS AND LAYERS OF CONSCIOUSNESS

In his 2010 book *Life Force, The Scientific Basis*, physicist Claude Swanson breaks down consciousness into a five-level hierarchy, which he calls 'Levels of Subtle Energy and Consciousness'. These levels are as follows:

- **Level Zero:** Ordinary Consciousness
  o regular everyday people
- **Level One:** Weak Subtle Energy
  o amateur energy healers, remote viewers, etcetera
- **Level Two:** Strong Subtle Energy
  o Qigong masters, Pranic healers, etcetera
- **Level Three:** Shamanic Healing
  o shamanic healers, adepts, etcetera
- **Level Four:** Higher Dimensional Consciousness
  o avatars, spirits, gurus, etcetera

I like this breakdown as it allows us to easily envision consciousness as a spectrum. Depending on where someone falls along that spectrum, their abilities to engage with subtle energy, and therefore transit between dimensions and realities is weaker or stronger. The higher on the spectrum someone is, the greater in-sync they are with the subtle energy of the universe. They become capable of crossing between phase states.

Let's dig into each level so we can get a better feel for them.

Level Zero Consciousness experiences no anomalies. Everything the senses pick up or perceive as reality adheres to the laws of physics as we know them and interference with or violation of those laws is statistically insignificant enough to be ignored completely or brushed off as coincidence. This level of consciousness is essentially the default of our human experience. It is incredibly hard to evolve beyond Level Zero Consciousness because it relies on a sort of collective bias. If we're taught that the paranormal is impossible or improbable in a culturally and academically systemic way, then we basically lock ourselves into our phase state. We are all synchronized so we never question that cohesion. We never dare to test the boundaries of what we think we know about reality. In rare circumstances, a particularly powerful moment (like an out-of-body or near-death experience, or a group meditative or ritual experience) can shake us out of synchronization and reveal what lies beyond, on the 'other side' of our reality. If enough people have these sorts of experiences, it becomes possible to shed our societal biases against the seemingly impossible, to break free of the group-think. Various cultures across the globe show us that this is possible. Qigong mastery across China is in part possible because enough people have bought into the idea that subtle energy *can* affect our reality. The same is true of many Indian and indigenous sub-cultures, who enjoy greater receptivity and openness to astral body experiences.

Level One Consciousness is basically the product of that openness and receptivity. People who fall into this level understand that subtle energy can affect the material, and physical world. Those who meditate fall into this category; they have a strong inner belief that their own energy can affect not only themselves but others around them. The Princeton PEAR Lab REG experiments we looked at in the last chapter provide a solid scientific backing for this level of consciousness. When enough people exert their spiritual, and psychological energy at a specific target, statistical anomalies present themselves clearly in the data. This is weak subtle energy and it presents itself in minor anomalies in our laws of physics, notable enough to make us question what other forces are really at work within the universe.

Level Two Consciousness takes the next leap. Rather than casual meditation or intentionality, individuals at this point on the spectrum are well-trained and practiced in energy manipulation. These include Qigong masters and Pranic healers. Anomalies are taken at face value and are rarely seen as coincidence or happenstance. This is strong subtle energy at work. The four fundamental forces of nature are seen to be challenged regularly. Those who experience reality at this level possess a strong enough understanding and control of subtle energy that their abilities can be accurately measured and registered by sophisticated laboratory equipment. Claude Swanson calls these 'cross-over points'—the ability of a master to exhibit "wide variations of synchronized phase". (Swanson, 2010)

Level Three Consciousness practitioners are capable of feats that we would associate with almost shamanic ability: instant healing, incidents verging on the miraculous, etcetera. This level of consciousness is more or less unexplainable by the laws of physics and would be considered impossible by most mainstream scientists. It requires that those who exercise subtle energy at this level be capable of drawing energy from some other place than simply from within. It requires an interdimensional skillset of the kind only history's greatest shamans are said to possess. In other words, the practitioner is synchronizing themselves with another phase state—another dimension. There exist credible, detailed accounts of abilities at this level. Among such accounts are the kahuna healers of

Hawaii and multiple Qigong healers across China who have apparently performed instantaneous bone healing... even the healing of scoliosis! (Long, 1948; Dong, 1997, 2006; Bartlett, 2007)

Finally, there is **Level Four Consciousness**. In this category, we would place the avatars and masters that, for the time being at least, we can only associate with myth and legend. For these powerful few, the laws of physics can be broken at whim. They exist as fully interdimensional beings, capable of shifting from one reality to the next in a totally decoherent way. Such beings would exist simultaneously across multiple realities. They could synchronize across all phases at will, using the full power of subtle energy as a literal passageway or bridge between dimensions. In essence, their consciousness exists completely outside our physical reality while still being a part of it. Figures assigned to this level of consciousness would include people like Jesus Christ and Buddha.

I have taken you through these levels of consciousness because they present a unique and ordered perspective of how the multiverse is psychologically accessible, conceptually speaking. Science fiction films and pop-cultural interpretations tend to reduce the multiverse to a simple parallel reality—there's a you in another part of the universe but with slightly different characteristics or lifestyle. This is ultimately simplistic for the purposes of entertainment, but it also reinforces the group-think that keeps us phase-locked in Level Zero Consciousness. It makes any deviation from the reality we think we know seem fanciful and unlikely. But it is exactly that rigidity of mind, body, and spirit that we must detach ourselves from in order to be receptive to the signals, frequencies, and wavelengths of subtle energy that are available to our consciousness.

Figure 6.9 *(Source: Pixabay, Creative Commons)* A visual representation of the auric energy field, or biofield, that surrounds the human body.

We can expand on Swanson's five levels by analyzing the layers of the aura. The aura is the energy field that surrounds living beings. (Hanegraaff, 2006) Scientists refer to it as an electromagnetic field, or 'biofield'. In the early 1900s, Dr. Walter J. Kilner developed a chemical screen process that enabled ordinary people to see the aura with the naked eye. (Kilner, 1911) Decades later, a more sophisticated understanding of the aura unfolded. Eastern European scientists developed ultraviolet cameras that could capture the UV radiation of the energy within the biofield. (Schleicher, 1988) Other techniques emerged as well. Yevgeniy Kulin worked on a technique to measure the electric field around the body. His research concluded that the aura is actually responsive to heartbeat and metabolism among other factors, and fluctuates greatly. By measuring the voltage of the biofield, he found fascinating correlations between the aura and the health of the subject. In other words, the healthier we are, the more energy is present in our aura. (Kulin, 1980) Similar voltage measurements have backed this up. American scientists studying the energy fields around living organisms have been able to predict health issues well in advance of symptoms developing by making note of disruptions in the biofield. One study looked for such disturbances in thousands of test subjects. One-hundred-and-two disturbances were found. Among those one-hundred-and-two people, further investigations confirmed that ninety-five of them had cancer. (Burr, 1972)

WHEN THE BIOPHOTONS ARE REFLECTED INTERNALLY, SOMETHING DOES ESCAPE: A TORSION WAVE

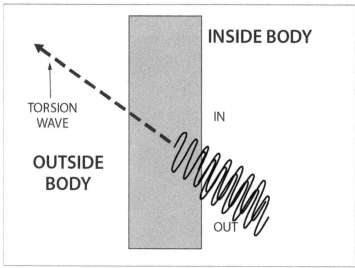

Figure 6.10 The torsion field carries the information about the biophotons inside the body to the outside of the body.

Another doctor by the name of Konstantin Korotkov invented a system called Gas Discharge Visualization (GDV) which digitally constructs aura readings based on electromagnetic measurements of the fingertips. The system has shown many applications, notably the mapping-out of energy across the whole body—including the torsion patterns unique to the energy in the biofield, as well as analyzing states of consciousness. The wider and further the biofield extends outside the body, the greater the out-of-body conditions are, and therefore, the higher the level of consciousness. (Korotkov, 2002, 2004)

Being able to account for the torsion field of the energy in our aura, as you have probably already guessed, is rather important when discussing our bodies, our consciousness, and our access to the subtle energy of the universe. It is believed that biophotons emitted by our bodies form a coherent pattern of torsion waves, that we can call the aura. "Biophotons are internally reflected inside the body [...] This keeps most of their energy inside the body, where it is needed [...] for biochemical reactions. But, there is something that is left over. Something escapes. That something is called 'torsion.'" (Swanson, 2010) The *information* imprinted in the biophotons is carried into the external biofield. This helps explain why disruptions or anomalies in that field can be indicative of poor health. Think of it this way: the biophotons inside the body have their own energy fields. Those fields are coherent with the external torsion fields. In other words, they are in the same phase state, and can therefore share the same information. Suddenly, the energy healing carried out by Qigong and Pranic masters makes a lot more sense, doesn't it? They are aligning their energy fields to match the phase state of the person they are projecting the energy to. They synchronize their vibrations and frequencies with their patient in the same way that they synchronize their conscious energy to that of the multiverse.

Clairvoyants and energy healers will tell you that the aura's purpose is to maintain the physical body, but they will also describe it as having layers. Each layer functions differently and is more visible when your consciousness accesses it. Because the aura can be viewed using ultraviolet cameras, each layer can be recognized by its colour. If you've ever had your aura read by someone, you'll recall them describing it in terms of colour—this is probably the most pop-culturally prevalent understanding of how the aura works. But casual, non-scientific readings aside, there is growing evidence that each layer coincides with higher dimensional reality perception. The layers exist as simultaneous planes of reality that the consciousness can access by tuning itself (or synchronizing itself) to a corresponding frequency. "When we enter a higher domain in full consciousness, it means our consciousness is synchronized with the vibrations of that plane. The higher planes have more complex motions and geometries than physical matter." (Shepherd, 1954; Swanson, 2010)

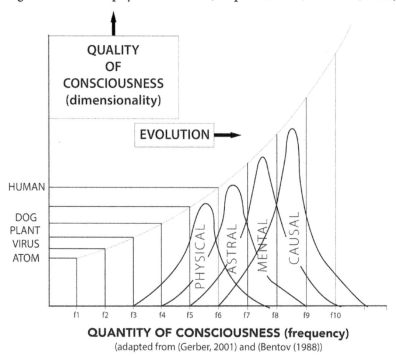

QUANTITY OF CONSCIOUSNESS (frequency)
(adapted from (Gerber, 2001) and (Bentov (1988))

Figure 6.11 Dimensionality to frequency ranges, separating the auric layers.

Many scientists have noted that the auric layers can be recognized by their distinct frequency ranges. Researchers like Richard Gerber and Itzak Bentov's work in this field has served as the foundation for identifying the intersections of *quality* of consciousness (dimensionality) and *quantity* of consciousness (frequency). The greater the frequency, the higher the dimensionality of our consciousness. These layers (or planes) are broken down as such: Etheric (Physical), Astral, Mental, Causal, and beyond that, Buddhic. I won't get too detailed, but let's review each layer so we can better understand its features. The details of each layer below are sourced from Claude Swanson's 2010 book *Life Force: The Scientific Basis*, as well as the aura-focussed works of Arthur E. Powell (1925, 1927, 1928, 1982).

The Etheric (or Physical) Layer extends only a few inches from the body surface. It regulates physical functions and exchanges energy in and out of the body. It directs growth and healing. Most of us exist within the energy fields of this layer, unaware that greater layers are accessible to our consciousness.

The Astral Layer extends about one to two feet from the body surface.

It regulates feelings, desires, and emotionality. As such, the stronger the emotion, the further this layer can extend beyond the body. It enables our sensations and allows for a connection between physical matter and higher-mindedness. Our consciousness goes to the Astral plane when we sleep, and this is why dreams are often hard to remember—dreams are not synchronized with our usual phase state. Remote viewers and those who have had out-of-body experiences make use of this layer.

The Mental Layer is five-dimensional. It is where consciousness and intellect merge and where our imagination and memories are stored. Individuals with higher consciousness can use this layer to transmit information to other individuals' mental auras. This is also the plane on which the Akashic Record I spoke of earlier can be accessed. This plane is all about cosmic information.

The Causal Layer is closely related to the Mental Layer but operates differently. Where the Mental Layer is focussed and specific, the Causal Layer is more abstract and formless. This plane is guided by causality and concerns itself with *how* and *why* things are the way they are. The experiences and wisdom we accumulate through our past lives and our present life are stored on this plane and they serve as both a record of our cosmic evolution and as a blueprint for how we navigate future experiences. It is for this reason that our manifesting power resides in the Causal Layer.

Finally, within the Buddhic Layer, our consciousness is able to overlap with that of others. Conscious individuality subsides and is replaced by a sensation of unity and limitless shared existence. On this plane, our consciousness is able to recognize itself in all others, even those we dislike or believe to be evil. We see others internally and can navigate their experiences from their point of view. This plane consists of love in its purest form. Space and time cease to have barriers on this plane, and simultaneous synchronicity across dimensions is possible.

You now have a strong sense of not only the layers of consciousness but the layers of the aura as well. With both in mind, you can see how accessing the auric layers provides the ability to achieve greater consciousness. The aura serves as a sort of vehicle of consciousness: it allows you to *travel* interdimensionally across planes of existence, through alternate and parallel realities. This is multiverse exploration. It is tuning the body to the subtle energy of the universe. And as you've seen, it's all about frequency and synchronization.

CROSSING OVER: THE OUT-OF-BODY EXPERIENCE

With all of this new knowledge in mind, let's go back to the yogi experiences we spoke of at the start of this chapter. What does it mean to *cross over*—to transit between planes and dimensions? What does it mean to travel the multiverse?

As I detailed before, two of the most recognizable and documented processes of interdimensional existence are out-of-body and near-death experiences. For someone of Level One Consciousness who exists within the Etheric Layer of their aura, OBEs and NDEs represent a kind of gateway or initiation to the multiverse. They cause the person experiencing them to open their eyes, often for the first time in their lives, to parallel or alternate realities that they had never envisioned before because their senses had never granted them the perception of the other side. For the purposes of this section, I will focus on OBEs, but similar phenomena and accounts have been reported by those who have had an NDE in their lifetime.

Perhaps no other researcher has dedicated as much time investigating OBEs as Robert Monroe, a scientist and engineer, whose own OBEs in the 1950s caused him to reevaluate reality as he knew it. How he got to that OBE is an interesting story in itself as it relates to the frequencies and energies that this book is focused on. For this reason, I think it's a story worth providing the background for...

While working on a technology that could electronically induce sleep, Monroe stumbled upon the powers of frequency. His technology was based on the principle that specific brain wave patterns were related to sleep. By introducing those patterns as sounds, he reasoned he could bring about a sleep state in the listener. This would prove to be part of the origin story of binaural beat therapy, which is now widely used to reduce stress and anxiety, as well as increase concentration, confidence, motivation, and more. It is also frequently used to encourage deeper states of meditation and enable higher states of consciousness. (Oster, 1973; Swanson, 2003) Essentially, two different tones (sound waves) are emitted (one in the left ear and another in the right ear) to entrain desired brain wave activity. Through a process of auditory illusion, the brain produces the perception of a third tone (a binaural beat), which has been shown to encourage brain wave changes specific to the tones used. Binaural beat therapies have been studied extensively in the field of mental health and meditation. (Le Scouarnec, 2001; Padmanabahn, 2005; Barling, 2003; Chaieb, 2015) Several studies have even found that this form of frequency therapy is capable of partially replacing the need for pharmaceutical anesthesia (fentanyl) during surgery! In other words, the frequencies inhibit the body's pain receptors to such a degree that the patient doesn't require pharmaceutical intervention. (Kliempt, 1999; Lewis, 2004)

To get back on track, you're probably asking how this led to an OBE for Robert Monroe. While testing his binaural beats one evening, Monroe closed his eyes as he laid down on his bed. When he opened his eyes, he suddenly found himself looking down at his own body from the ceiling. His consciousness had left his body and he was seeing himself from a detached, astral state. Thinking he was hallucinating, dying, or simply going crazy, he sought a medical exam when he had returned to his normal, physical state. His doctor gave him the all-clear. As he continued to test his technology, he continued to have more OBEs. They became more pronounced and he was able to sustain them for longer periods of time. He claims in many of these astral journeys, he could move to other parts of his property, and even other parts of the country, where he was able to observe people he knew. He had never heard of an OBE before having them but soon learned that in other cultures, especially older and Eastern cultures, OBEs are well-documented and considered a relatively normal experience. (Monroe, 1971, 1985, 1994) As he refined his technology, he was able to isolate specific frequencies which could take him on his astral journeys, and even tailor his *travels* to particular levels of consciousness. (Swanson, 2003)

Figure 6.12 (Source: unknown) Image of the Monroe Institute campus in Faber, Virginia.

Years of tinkering led to the founding of the Monroe Institute in 1978, whose work I've mentioned previously in this book. There, research has been conducted with all sorts of individuals, and often in collaboration with major organizations like U.S. government agencies (CIA, DIA, etcetera). The remote viewers in the Stargate Project were among those who spent time at the Monroe Institute (Schnabel, 1997) The immense body of work the Monroe Institute has accumulated over the decades is some of the most powerful evidence of subtle energy's ability to enhance the human mind, body, and spirit—to enable personal evolution with the intent to become truly superhuman. As Robert Monroe himself wrote in his 1994 book *Ultimate Journey*, "Exploration out-of-body is a prime means of functioning outside the physical universe. The 'second body' of the OB state is certainly not physical. It is part of another energy system that commingles with the Earth Life System but is out of phase with it. The clue lies in how easy it is to find those who have left physical existence."

Many of those who have had their own OBEs or who research them in the field of parapsychology and paraphysics believe that when undergoing an OBE, we actually find ourselves in a parallel version of our own world—a sort of mirror image that is less stable than the physical world we usually inhabit. (Rogo, 1983) Some describe encountering portals within the parallel realities that they visit, 'spatial openings' as physicist J.H.M. Whiteman called them in his 1961 book *The Mystical Life*. These are believed to be tunnels between dimensions or realms, perhaps only accessible if the person experiencing the OBE is at a high enough level of consciousness. (Swanson, 2003)

Studies have shown that when someone experiences an OBE state, their electromagnetic readings demonstrate wild fluctuation: brain wave activity, physiological functions, etcetera, deviate from their normal resting states. This tells us that consciousness is intrinsically tied to energy and the electromagnetic structure of our bodies and minds. Energy, from a purely physics-oriented perspective (in accordance with the laws of physics as we know them) can be modulated, manipulated, and adjusted. It can be affected by an endless list of variables. This suggests that our consciousness can be controlled if we can harness subtle energy. And knowing that there are multiple levels of reality, alternate and parallel dimensions, entire universes... all accessible through higher consciousness, it stands to reason that we can *manifest* the reality we desire, that we can align our intentions with our outcomes.

Like the *choose-your-own-adventure* novels we read as kids, by tapping into universal subtle energy (the cosmic web) we can choose our own timeline. We can exist simultaneously across dimensions, just as the yogis we talked about earlier do. We can bend the physical world to our mind's vision. "Consciousness seems to have a power over matter when this deep perspective is understood. To a yogi, the physical levels of the universe are seen as only the lowest level of a hierarchy of dimensions, and they develop the ability to move effortlessly between and within such dimensions. They are now focusing on the higher spiritual layers and their own evolvement. Manifestation of the physical is child's play once its *understanding is fully comprehended*." (Swanson, 2003)

MANIFESTATION

"Conditions, thoughts, activities of men in every clime are things; as thoughts are things. They make their impression upon the skein of time and space. Thus, as they make for their activity, they become as records that may be read by those in accord or attuned to such a condition... For thoughts are things." (Cayce, 1971)

Thoughts are things. Perhaps you have a vision board at home: a collection of images, phrases, quotes, and ideas that represent your desires, your intentions, and your dreams. Maybe you have a bucket list: a series of things you'd like to do, see, or acquire in your lifetime. Or perhaps you rely on prayer, as a part of your faith, to realize your vision for yourself. All of these practices rely on visualization. If you can imagine it for yourself, then it is achievable. Most of us have been told this or something similar from the time we're small children. But the science of visualization suggests that when we desire something strongly enough, when we double down mentally on our intentions, we actually modify the photon background in the space-time around us. We affect the energy in our biofield, our aura. This change in energy is measurable, detectable, and with some instruments, it's even visible. The REG experiments we looked at in Chapter 5, which were performed thousands of times over, prove that intention, even by those with no consciously adept abilities, has the power to influence physical matter. In fact, "visualization of the event increases the likelihood that it will happen." (Swanson, 2003)

Visualization then is a mechanism or tool that we can use to manifest not only our personal evolution, but the events and experiences we wish to live out. Prayers, thoughts, and wishes are not just non-physical aberrations of the mind. They are frequencies that we emit. Our biofields register these emissions, and if our consciousness is open and receptive, we can transmit those frequencies—that energy, to a desired outcome in space-time. Famed theoretical physicist John Archibald Wheeler, who coined such terms as 'black hole' and 'wormhole', was a proponent of this interconnected, interdimensional framework of energy exchange. He believed that the universe is not just something *out there*, beyond and independent of us and our consciousness. Rather, he said that we are inextricably involved in creating the world around us. "We are not only observers. We are participators." The universe itself, he said, is *participatory*, and if physics is to answer the greatest questions we have about life and consciousness, he argued that we must start demanding that physics understand existence itself. (Brian, 2001)

Manifestation is often understood as the Law of Attraction: that positive or negative thoughts bring about positive or negative outcomes through a process of projected energy attracting similar energy in return. In this chapter, we've come to understand this process as the synchronization of phase states, and the matching of vibrational patterns. As Buddha said, "All that we are is the result of what we have thought. The mind is everything. What we think, we become." Wheeler held a similar view, but through the lens of quantum physics: "Spacetime tells matter how to move; matter tells spacetime how to curve." (Wheeler, 1998) In other words, our physical, material minds can exert energy that curves (or shapes) our reality.

Wheeler, in conjunction with mathematical physicist Sir Roger Penrose, was among those who established a forward-thinking subset of physics research that proposes that consciousness is a product of quantum mechanics – that the universe itself has a quantum consciousness. (Taylor, 2010) Wheeler shared a belief in Hugh Everett's 'universal wavefunction', basically a universal phase state, which serves as the core concept of the 'many-worlds interpretation' (MWI). The MWI asserts that the likelihood of uncountable, infinite universes is a probable certainty, and views time as a branched tree, where every conceivable quantum outcome is possible and realizable. (Osnaghi, 2009; Everett, 1957, 1973)

In his 2010 book about *decoding* the Law of Attraction, aerospace engineer Travis Taylor points out that reality is unique to each individual. When you have a thought, a new wave function of energy is created. This wave function ripples outward and extends into the universe, interacting with every other wave function in the same phase state. Your energy entangles with the energy of the universe, and this entanglement, or cohesion, creates your reality. If you can learn to train your thoughts (your energy), then you can produce energy that coheres with the energy of the outcome you're looking for. As Taylor says, "Don't generate [energy] that says, 'I always get stuck in traffic,' unless that is the outcome you desire."

Quantum physicist Fred Alan Wolf's work specializes in the relationship between physics and consciousness. His 1981 book *Taking the Quantum Leap* used a simple experiment to demonstrate, at a very small scale, how you can train your mind to produce different realities. The experiment is a simple line-drawing of a box, as seen below...

Take a close look at Figure 6.13. Which side of the box is open? The top? The front? The sides? The bottom? None of them? If you see one side as open, can you encourage your brain to forget about that, and to see another side as open? Give it a try. *Force* your brain to see the box in a new way. Have you done it? Okay... now let's go a step further. Focus... and make the box disappear. After all, it's not really a box. It's not even three-dimensional. It's *just* a series of two-dimensional lines that your

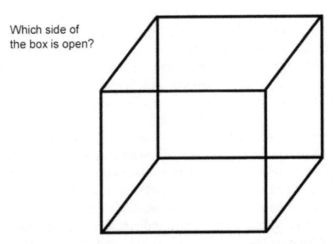

Which side of
the box is open?

Figure 6.13 *(Taylor, 2010, as described from Wolf, 1981, license unknown)*
Wolf's thought experiment encourages the viewer to challenge their
mind to see multiple realities—which side of the box is open?

brain is being tricked into viewing as three-dimensional. Can you see it as
just that though—as *just* a series of lines? Now go back and forth. Open,
closed, not a box at all, back to a box again. Do it really fast, as fast as you
can. Over and over. It's hard, isn't it? But why?

You see, a single thought typically exists in the mind for only a few
milliseconds. So in order to see what you want to see in the drawing of
the box, you have to produce a 'train of thought', a series of replicating,
sustained, identical thoughts. "If we maintain this focus, we are sending
out the same wave function into the universe. The more we send this wave
function into the universe, the more likely it is that this wave function will
interact and cohere with a wave function similar to it. And the result will
be a reality that we desire." (Taylor, 2010) Manifestation.

Some scientists call the underlying phenomenon of this process
'universal quantum connection', the principle being that we are quantum
connected to all things across time and space. Think back to the Akashic
Record: the vibrational patterns of everything that has ever happened
across the cosmos encoded on distant matter in the universe. A sort of
fingerprint of time and space. If we can tune our minds to see Wolf's
box any way we please (creating simultaneous realities), then we can
tune our minds to receive and transmit the subtle energy that makes up
the quantum universe. As a long-time student of martial arts myself, I
particularly enjoy the way Travis Taylor analogizes this tuning in. He asks
us to imagine that we are all white belts on our first day of class. Our
bare feet have just touched the mat for the first time and we are learning
the basics of energy, the cosmic web, the multiverse, and the universal
quantum connection... Through preparation, study, work, focus, and

intention, we can each move our way from beginner to master. We can achieve the black or red belt status that we seek, and that status goes beyond just understanding the concepts and subjects that we've been discussing in this book. That status enables us to *apply* that understanding. Knowing things makes one academic. Applying them makes one a practitioner.

Manifestation can be practiced in many ways, but the science tells us that it is more than just *thinking positively* or having *good karma*. The process of manifesting our desires is not just about having the initial thought, but training the mind to sustain a train of thought that can express itself as a wave function—as subtle energy. The process of manifesting is about entanglement, cohesion, and synchronicity through higher, interdimensional consciousness. And even though it may sound complex, it is within each of our individual powers to harness this universal truth.

CHAPTER IN REVIEW

In this chapter, we explored the multiverse and how it can be travelled using consciousness. We looked at how accessing parallel and alternative dimensions, worlds, and timelines is a matter of synchronizing our own energy with that of the subtle energy that makes up the majority of the universe. We took a peek through the *trap doors* of conscious and auric levels and took a walk in the shoes of those who have had out-of-body experiences. And we came to the same conclusion that each of the chapters in this book has come to thus far: that energy is the secret. Whether it be understanding how the cosmos work, or making the cosmos work in alignment with our intentions, subtle energy (in all its wavelengths and frequencies) is the key to unlocking not only the secrets of reality but the reality that we desire.

In his 1980 television series *Cosmos: A Personal Journey*, the legendary astrophysicist Carl Sagan said, "The cosmos is within us. We are made of star-stuff. We are a way for the universe to know itself." To manifest our reality then—to truly shape our outcomes, we must allow the universe to know us as well as it can, for, in that synchronization, we can find the superhuman within us all. We can be our own Qi master.

And that's what the next chapter is about. I'm going to share with you the incredible technologies that I've been developing through the years. I'll introduce you to devices and resources that will allow you to harness the subtle energy within and around you. With the right tools at your disposal, there's no stopping how far you can take your personal evolution. The goal of making such cosmic journeys possible has been the focus of my life's work. Everything you've read so far has compiled knowledge and awareness. I hope I've opened your eyes to the true nature of reality. As you turn through the pages of this next chapter, I will take you through the technologies my company has been working on, and share with you the powerful ways they can transform your life for the better. Your Qi Life awaits...

———————————

Are you ready to dip your toes into the multiverse? Higher states of consciousness are closer, and easier to access than you may think. And with them comes the ability to use interdimensional knowledge to manifest your ideal outcomes. Meditation is one of the best ways to access these alternate conscious realities, but we don't all have the time to become energy masters, gurus, or monks.

My team and I have spent years developing frequencies that can put your mind in a state of deep meditation. Think of it as a shortcut or cheat-code. You can actualize self-happiness without unhealthy habits or validation from others. You can identify blockages without expensive courses or retreats. You can develop strong willpower and purpose without needing motivation or a costly life coach.

Our frequencies are tuned to contain mathematical representations of various states of higher consciousness. You can use them on their own, or amplify them by using our devices, like the Qi Coil™, to convert their sound signatures into electromagnetic and quantum energy.

Tune up your chakra, attract positive energy, clear Qi blockages, increase intuition, cleanse your thoughts... and so much more. Your pathway to deep transformation starts with synchronizing your own frequency with that of the subtle energy of the universe. We've developed the tools and resources that can jumpstart that process.

>>> **Visit www.HigherQuantum.com to download the world's most powerful meditation frequencies.**

SCAN ME!

CHAPTER 7
QI ENERGY TECHNOLOGY

The amazing power of resonant frequency has been at the center of every chapter of this book. It's been the universe's best-kept secret, and yet, civilization after civilization, a knowing few have come to the same conclusion over and over again: Qi energy is the answer. It's the golden thread that ties everything together. When I first came to this realization so many years ago, it rocked me to my core, and I couldn't believe that more people weren't aware of it and that more scientists weren't exploring it. I knew at that moment that my calling was to spread that awareness and to engage in that exploration.

Through years of hard work and perseverance, my team has put together a collection of some of the best energy-based products and therapy resources on the market today. We've built upon the wisdom of ancient masters and the ingenuity of scientific pioneers who have come before us to improve upon their knowledge and discoveries. In this chapter, I will take you through the four key areas of energy therapy that my team and I are the most excited about: sound therapy, light therapy, P.E.M.F. therapy, and quantum resonance therapy. We'll look back through the pages of history to understand how each therapy came into being, and I'll reveal how my team has evolved them all.

Across these four areas of focus, we've developed cutting-edge devices to help deliver their respective benefits. But we didn't just stop there. We've also pushed the boundaries of what each of these therapeutic technologies can achieve. We're moving the goalposts of this new frontier in science and doing our part to push the energy revolution forward, one frequency at a time. We believe Qi energy is transformational. *You* can transform *your* wellness, *your* abundance, *your* body, *your* mind, and yes... *you* can transform *your* reality.

SOUND THERAPY

You've had a bad day at work. Nothing went right. Your coworkers drove you up the wall. Your boss was hard on you. Five o'clock comes around and you're finally back in your car, ready to drive home. You turn on the radio. One of your favorite songs is playing... and as you leave the parking lot, your mood is already starting to improve.

You're taking a walk along the beach. It's a warm summer's night. The waves are lapping at your feet as they crash to shore. Seagulls are squawking in the distance. There's a couple up ahead sitting in the sand; one of them is playing guitar. They've got a bonfire going in front of them. Suddenly, another wave is washing over you: a wave of calmness and tranquillity.

You've just heard some bad news. Maybe someone you know has fallen ill, or that weekend away has fallen through, or your friend can't come to visit you from out of town anymore. You make a cup of tea and head outside to sit on the patio. A hummingbird zooms in from out of nowhere and buzzes around you. It hangs in the air and that fast-paced whir of its tiny wings brings a smile to your face.

You're at the gym. You're starting to fade, but that workout playlist you made is finally starting to get good. The theme music from Rocky comes on and all of a sudden, that fatigue melts away. You can break through the physical barrier that only moments before had you wanting to quit. Your inner Sly Stallone is ready for that last burn of glory before calling it a day.

Even when you're not specifically seeking it out, *sound* has a way of shifting your attitude, quieting your mind, changing your disposition, comforting you in a time of need, transporting you to a special memory, reminding you of your favorite movie, reinvigorating your energy, or even putting you in that *special* mood with that special someone.... Sound is everywhere, and while admittedly, not all sounds are good (some are just noise, even), others have the power to be transformative. Our emotions, our spirits, and even our bodies can react positively to the right sounds at

Figure 7.1 *(Source: QiLifeStore.com)* Photo of a woman using the Qi Coil™ system for electromagnetic therapy.

the right times. We've all experienced this, but have you ever stopped to think about it? Have you ever stopped to ask yourself questions like...

Can I use sound proactively? Can I use it to heal? Can I use it to focus? Can I use it to relax? Can I use it to target my specific needs?

The answer to all these questions, as I'm sure you've already guessed, is a resounding yes... or should I say a *resonant* yes. After all, what is sound? Sound is just vibrations that manifest themselves as acoustic waves. For living beings, sound is the reception of those waves, as perceived by our brains. (Western Electrical Company, 1969) Not all living beings perceive the same range of audio frequencies. Humans can hear sound wavelengths that fall between 20Hz and 20kHz, give or take a few hertz. We don't have the best ears in the animal kingdom (not by a longshot, in fact), but no other living being on this planet *enjoys* sound as much as humans. Since the dawn of our existence, we've gone out of our way to play with sound, to experiment with it, to mix different tones, to vocalize melodically, and so much more. That old Beach Boys song was on to something: the sounds we like are quite literally 'good vibrations'.

Figure 7.2 *(Source: Wikipedia, photo by Swarnima Shrestha, Creative Commons)*
Photo of a Nepalese 'singing bowl' taken near a monument in Nepal.

It should come as no surprise then that sound has healing properties. A recent special report in The Globe and Mail documented one research psychologist's academic sound journey. The University of California San Diego's Tamara Goldsby, who works in integrative health, encountered a man from Nepal at an outdoor market. He had a wooden mallet and was moving it around the inside of a peculiar metal bowl. This motion created a "beautiful clear sound". The instrument is known as a 'singing bowl' or 'standing bell', and its use dates as far back as the Shang dynasty, between the 16th and 11th centuries BCE. Their purpose is to generate low-frequency sounds that calm the nervous system and elicit feelings of calm and relaxation. Having had a memorable experience meeting this man from Nepal, Goldsby initiated a study which concluded that sustained, low-frequency sounds result in the reduction of symptoms of pain, lowered anxiety, tension, and anger, and improved feelings of depression. The study also found evidence for an increase in spiritual well-being. (Price, 1983; Goldsby, 2016; Sharratt, 2019)

Lee Bartel, a professor at the University of Toronto's Faculty of Music carried out similar research and found that sound therapy is effective in the improvement of Alzheimer's disease symptoms—as much as a 13% increase in cognitive skills. His work also found beneficial results for those suffering from fibromyalgia, and demonstrated mood and reaction time improvements in those with depression. Bartel's studies show that sound therapy has the ability to stimulate neurons in the brain, strengthening neural circuitry. By opening these cognitive pathways, the brain can better regulate itself, and in turn, so can the body overall. (Bartel, 2016; 2019a; 2019b)

These studies are just a tiny sample of an exhaustive list of research that could be referenced on the subject of sound therapy. And that's not even including the historical examples that could be examined, like the chanting and mantric recitations that have been a part of the traditions of Hinduism for thousands of years, to name just one example. Sound therapy generates sonic vibrations that regenerate cognitive and physical well-being. The science on this has been broad and conclusive for quite some time.

As Bartel points out, many illnesses and diseases are the result of dysregulation of the brain and body. In other words, an imbalance. As you've learned in this book, every cell in our body has its own frequency and spin. This natural vibration is known as resonance. Many researchers agree that sound therapy (sonic vibration) has the ability to revert imbalanced frequencies back to their natural resonance. Sound can re-regulate the dysregulation of imbalanced resonance. And it can do this so effectively in part because our bodies are made up of 60% water, which is one of nature's greatest conductors of sound. This is why music and sound have such a powerful effect on us. We naturally conduct their good vibes at the cellular level. Mainstream medicine has made very few attempts to integrate this valuable and powerful therapy into its care regimens. I see this as a major error in the medical field's judgement.

This gap in preventative, reparative, and rehabilitative care is where my products come into play. We've curated a sophisticated and diverse collection of healing frequencies that use the power of sound waves to help the body heal itself by encouraging the body's natural homeostasis. What's that, you ask? Homeostasis is your body's natural internal regulation of physical and chemical conditions. Your body is constantly at work tweaking and adjusting your internal functions in order to maintain optimal equilibrium. (Betts, 2013; Martin, 2008) As we've covered extensively, the quest for energy in balance, sync, and harmony is the ultimate end goal of answering the secrets of the universe… but so too is that quest a major component in revealing the secrets of truly revolutionary healthcare and wellness.

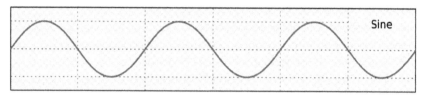

Figure 7.3 *(Source: Wikipedia, Creative Commons)* Visual representation of a sine wave.

Our technology breaks sound down into one of its simplest forms: sine waves. Sine waves are a form of smooth, continuous sound. They represent a singular frequency with no harmonics. Think of the tone you hear when you pick up a landline telephone. That's an example of a sine wave. These sound waves can be programmed to take on different oscillation and amplitude patterns, with each variation tailored to achieve a different physical or cognitive outcome. Your brain can lock onto these sound waves and synchronize with their resonance. This process is called neural or brainwave entrainment. Essentially, the large-scale electrical oscillations inside your brain (your brainwaves) synchronize to the rhythm of the external sonic stimulus. (Thaut, 2015)

Research in this field dates back to as early as 1665 with experiments performed by physicist Christiaan Huygens, and 1875 with experiments by physiologist Richard Caton, to name just a few. Each additional trial, study, and experiment since has added to the evidence that different states of consciousness can be achieved through acoustic or sonic brainwave entrainment. (Pantaleone, 2002; Berger, 1929; Cantor, 2013; Diep, 2019; Niedermeyer, 2004) The oscillations inside your brain and throughout your central nervous system are rhythmic and repetitive, and are heavily correlative with emotional response, memory, perception, information transmission, and motor control. (Fries, 2005; Fell, 2011; Schnitzler, 2005) One of the easiest and most visual ways to know that your brain is responsive to entrainment is to watch your fingers and toes when you're around music being played. Ever notice them start to tap along to the beat? That's your brain waves synchronizing with external sound waves!

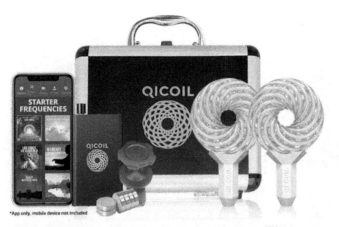

Figure 7.4 *(Source: QiLifeStore.com)* The portable Qi Coil™ 3s system, with carrying case, therapeutic magnets and mobile Qi Coil App.

My devices, such as the Qi Coil™ and Aura Coil™ emit these powerful, healing, entraining sound waves. You can choose from a wide array of unique, dedicated harmonic sound frequencies from our beautiful Qi App interface. Each frequency is designed to stimulate a different physical or cognitive entrainment outcome. The primary focus of this technology is to encourage a strong relaxation response. Once the brain enters a meditative state, it will naturally activate homeostatic processes, which will bring your body into equilibrium. But more than this, in a meditative state, your body is better positioned to tap into the subtle energy around you because its ability to send and receive signals is heightened. Sound therapy is one of the best gateways to enabling synchronicity and phase state alignment in order to access higher states of consciousness and superhuman abilities.

Our users have experienced amazing physical and cognitive benefits using our coil devices and their sound therapy features:

- Reduce anxiety and depression
- Increase feelings of relaxation and calmness
- Enhance your ability to adapt and cope with stress
- Relieve tension, headaches, insomnia, and pain
- Improve focus
- Better your memory and recall
- Increase energy and stamina
- Increase circulation for better cell function
- Elevate levels of oxygen throughout the body
- Speed up recovery times

Figure 7.5 *(Source: QiLifeStore.com)* Qi Coil™ users experiencing
the power of soothing magnetic waves.

And these benefits (and more) can all be supercharged by incorporating our quantum and higher quantum frequencies into your sound therapy routine. Our quantum variants are our most powerful, scientifically proven to help you experience the deepest levels of meditation. These frequencies are tuned to the resonant frequencies of the Earth, sea, sun, moon, and many other powerful celestial bodies. Their unique electromagnetic acoustics will allow you to tune your biofield more precisely.

Best of all, all of our sound therapy tools are easy to use, safe for almost everyone, and can be undertaken at home, at the office, and even on the go thanks to the ultra-portability of devices like the Qi Coil™, which is so innovative that it requires no calibration or technological know-how whatsoever. If you can use a smartphone or tablet, you can use a Qi Coil™. The healing powers of sound therapy take only a few days for the brain and body to begin entraining themselves. In general, thirty minutes of listening twice a day for about a week is all it takes for your system to acclimate and adjust. We recommend a month of use to begin getting the most out of this powerful technology. It's around this point that the most noticeable differences in your state of mind and overall health start to be readily apparent. This is especially true for conditions like insomnia and chronic pain.

LIGHT THERAPY

Like sound, light is an external stimulus that our body and brain react to with a wide range of responses, both good and bad. The warm glow of a sunrise or sunset can make us feel a sense of wonder and connection with nature. We are more productive on a sunny day than on a rainy one. We all prefer the diffused light of a lamp to the harsh light of overhead lighting. Lighting can make or break good landscaping or architecture. It can excite us like laser shows and fireworks displays do. It can also harm some of us, like the way flashing lights can induce a seizure in someone with epilepsy, or the way looking directly at the sun or an eclipse can damage our eyes. Perhaps you or someone you know suffers annually from seasonal affective disorder (SAD), which is a form of depressive mood response to the darker, drearier lighting that typically comes along with the winter months. (Oginska, 2014)

And what is *light*, exactly? Well, like sound, it's energy! Light is electromagnetic radiation, which, like sound, presents itself in wavelengths. Light exists on a spectrum between infrared and ultraviolet. Light is composed of and made possible by photons. (CIE, 1987; Buser, 1992) As you'll recall from the previous chapter, our bodies (and all biological entities on Earth) produce internal biophotons, which are associated with our biofields (auras). For this reason, light therapy is about more than just physical treatments. It's also about the treatment and regulation of our conscious and spiritual well-being.

Figure 7.6 *(Source: QiLifeStore.com)*
Red light therapy being used for various functions.

We are susceptible to so many different light inputs and stimuli, and just like the sounds that surround us, lighting is often taken for granted or ignored, particularly in mainstream healthcare. But light, when used therapeutically, can transform our bodies and brains in highly effective and beneficial ways. These can range from solving simple vitamin D deficiency, improving skin conditions like acne, dermatitis, psoriasis, eczema, and vitiligo, speeding up wound healing, repairing retinal damage, treating depression, sleep disorders, and jet lag, addressing neonatal jaundice in newborns, and so much more. (Lee, 2014; Pei, 2015; Patrizi, 2015; Diffey, 1980; Bae, 2017; Bouzari, 2012; Arden, 2012; Tuunainen, 2004; Bjorvatn, 2009; Dodson, 2010; Newman, 2009) There's even evidence that ultraviolet light is effective at combating certain types of cancer! (Morton, 2002)

Light therapy is hardly a new concept. The ancient Egyptian, Greek, Roman, Incan, Assyrian, Chinese, Indian, and Germanic peoples all have documented uses of light in their written or illustrated records, some dating back as far as 1500 BCE—particularly for medical and healing purposes. (Ellinger, 1957) Modern light therapy (using artificial light) was the product of physician and scientist Niels Finsen, who won the 1903 Nobel Prize in Physiology or Medicine for his work in the field. His use of light focussed on treating smallpox lesions with red light and treating tuberculosis with filtered ultraviolet light. (Moller, 2014) Natural light therapy (i.e. being outside in the sun) was a common course of treatment for patients during the first half of the 20th century. (Woloshyn, 2017) It was during the 1930s that Royal Rife, whose work we've covered before, also dabbled in light therapy, when he experimented with strong, colored light targeting certain microbes. (Lynes, 1987)

Light therapy comes in many variations. Not all kinds are available for home or personal use, but for the sake of painting a picture of just how versatile healing light can be, let's explore a few examples. Afterward, I'll tell you about the exciting devices my team has come up with, and which kind of light therapies we're focusing on at the moment. Photodynamic therapy uses nontoxic, light-sensitive compounds to target diseased cells. When light is applied, the compounds activate and become toxic. (Dougherty, 1998) This technique is commonly used to treat optical and skin conditions, malignant cancers, and has even shown to be effective as an antiviral treatment for conditions like herpes. (Wang, 2002) Another variation, called intense pulsed light therapy, is used for cosmetic and skin-related purposes like hair removal and skin rejuvenation. (Belenky, 2015) It is also used in the treatment of many eye conditions. (Toyos, 2015) Low-level laser therapy is another form. It uses light-emitting diodes (LEDs) on the surface of the skin to treat such issues as fibromyalgia, arthritis, carpal tunnel syndrome, chronic pain, joint disorders, and to speed up wound healing. It's also been shown to reduce the negative side effects of chemotherapy. (Brosseau, 2010; Huang, 2015; Chow, 2009; Cobb, 2006; Da Silva, 2010; Oberoi, 2014) Low-level laser therapy is even used for veterinarian purposes for various canine and feline conditions. (Robinson, 2013) Blood irradiation therapy is another kind of light therapy. It exposes blood to ultraviolet light with the purpose of eradicating viruses and bacteria, and to activate the immune system. (Knott, 1948, Hamblin, 2017; Geynitz, 2012) Finally, light box or light therapy lamps provide an additional form of light therapy. They are most commonly used to address seasonal affective disorder and sleep disorders, and have also shown to be effective at treating mood disorders and depression. (Lazzerini Ospry, 2017; Harrison, 2015)

With so many uses already a part of modern medicine, light therapy is one of the areas where energy healing is considered a part of normal, everyday treatment. To me, this shows that when people understand how energy works, they can overcome the mainstream stigma that is so often associated with innovative, energy-based approaches. That openness is a source of inspiration to me and my team. When we began developing our Qi Life light therapy devices, we wanted to produce something that was easy to use, but still offered the broadest possible therapeutic benefits. Hot-laser and high-intensity light therapy are obviously best carried out by a professional medical practitioner, but lower-intensity therapies, which are usually carried out at clinics and spas can absolutely be performed on your own from the comfort of your home, office, or even on the go. For this reason, we've prioritized low-level laser therapy, using red light and infrared light, and crafted devices that push these therapies to the next level. No more travelling to a practitioner or booking expensive appointments. You're in control, and you can use light therapy whenever you wish.

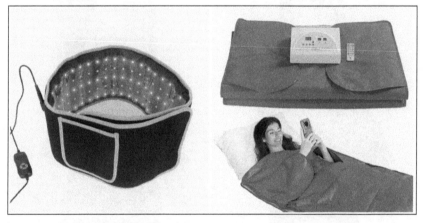

Figure 7.7 (Source: QiLifeStore.com)
The Qi LITE Red Light Therapy Belt and Infrared Sauna Blanket.

Our Qi LITE™ Red Light Therapy Belt is designed specifically with weight-loss stimulation in mind, by targeting and optimizing your metabolism. Using the Qi LITE™ Therapy Belt for just thirty minutes provides the equivalent of burning three-thousand calories—the same as jogging for an hour, swimming or doing yoga for thirty minutes, or doing two-hundred sit-ups. But the benefits don't stop there. The Qi LITE™ Therapy Belt offers a whole host of additional benefits with its powerful red light capabilities:

- Increase blood circulation
- Prevent varicose veins

- Relieve sore muscles
- Reduce inflammation and swelling
- Reduce strain and fatigue
- Alleviate joint and arthritis pain
- Accelerate wound healing
- Diminish scars and burns
- Increase post-workout recovery times
- Boost lymphatic drainage

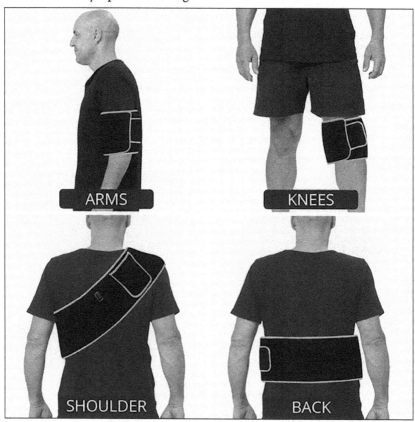

Figure 7.8 *(Source: QiLifeStore.com)*
The Qi LITE Red Light Therapy Belt in use.

Integrative red light therapy works from the inside-out to enhance mitochondrial function in cells, to shield against negative energy, and to prevent energy depletion. It adopts the principle of modern infrared light treatment, combined with the theories of acupuncture and moxibustion found in traditional Chinese medicine (the original light acupuncture), and light circulation therapy, to provide you with the most effective means to alleviate your pain. And the Qi LITE™ Therapy Belt can be used all over your body, allowing you to easily target its light healing to where you need it most.

Figure 7.9 *(Source: QiLifeStore.com)*
The Infrared Sauna Blanket in use.

Our Infrared Sauna Blanket brings the powerful benefits of infrared light therapy from the clinics and spas into your home, like never before. Infrared saunas have become massively popular in recent years, but with popularity comes scarcity. Booking an appointment can be a major hassle, and that's not even counting the commute times involved. At-home infrared light therapy is a luxury you can finally afford. Slip into this sleeping-bag-like system and enjoy a full range of infrared benefits:

- Detox and cleanse the body through sweat induction
- Burn calories
- Boost and strengthen your immune system
- Reduce stress and decrease cortisol levels
- Raise your serotonin levels
- Increase your metabolism
- Boost collagen for natural, glowing skin
- Improve sleep patterns and restfulness
- Improve blood circulation

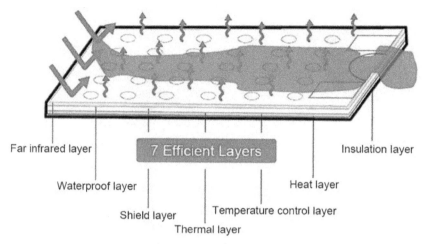

Far infrared layer

7 Efficient Layers

Insulation layer

Waterproof layer

Heat layer

Shield layer

Temperature control layer

Thermal layer

Figure 7.10 *(Source: QiLifeStore.com)* The Infrared Sauna Blanket has seven layers, each designed to enhance your at-home sauna experience.

Using the Infrared Sauna Blanket for just thirty minutes provides the equivalent benefits of running or swimming for an hour, doing yoga for thirty minutes, or doing one-hundred sit-ups. With its integrated temperature control protector, you can rely on constant temperature dispersion and safety. And with a zipper that goes all the way around, you can easily get in and out, as well as clean the inside.

Our devices exert ranges of 600-660nm and 800-880nm wavelengths. You'll love the *feel-good* endorphins that both our Belt and Blanket systems provide. Pain management, inflammation control, expedited recovery, increased mobility, and cell regeneration are some of the most effective ways to relieve physical discomfort and stress—and light therapy is the best way to achieve all these goals and more.

These systems, as well as our other light therapy devices, all make use of the amazing benefits of light energy wavelengths to bring about powerful physical and cognitive betterment and balance. By synchronizing our internal biophotons with external photon energy, we can safely and effectively treat a broad host of ailments, illnesses, disorders, and spiritual blockages. We can encourage and stimulate deeper meditative states, and in so doing, we can achieve the higher states of consciousness that only energy healing can provide.

P.E.M.F. THERAPY (ELECTROMAGNETISM)

As we discussed in the previous chapter, your body has its own electromagnetic field: the biofield, or aura. This field is influenced by external frequencies all day long—what scientists call 'electromagnetic pollution'. This constant bombardment of energy can take its toll. Your body is home to trillions of cells and each one produces its own electromagnetic field, communicating with other cells by electromagnetic frequency. This exchange of electromagnetic energy keeps your body *in* or *out* of balance by controlling your body's chemical processes. When these processes are negatively disrupted in some way, undesirable effects can occur. But if these processes are positively reinforced, stimulated, or enhanced, the effects can be noticeably beneficial. But how can you proactively engage your biofield? By immersing yourself in a pulsed electromagnetic field (P.E.M.F.). P.E.M.F. therapy involves devices which generate electromagnetic fields around the user in order to stimulate desired physical and cognitive responses.

The origins of this technology actually find root in magnetic field therapy. For millennia, magnets and their powers of attraction and repulsion have frequently been used for their natural healing forces. Ancient Chinese, Indian, and Greek healers used magnetic lodestones (naturally magnetized mineral magnetite) to manipulate imbalances of energy flow as part of their medical practices. (Sivin, 1988, 1993; Zysk, 1993; Frawley, 2001; Emerson, 2019) Even Queen Elizabeth I's physician, Sir William Gilbert, who is often said to be the father of electrical science, used magnets to ease the Queen's arthritis pains. (Thompson, 1903) Historical uses of magnetic field therapy include general pain relief, reduction of inflammation, improved sleep, the treatment of infections, stress relief, improved circulation, etcetera. (Lawrence, 1998) From a scientific perspective, these uses made perfect sense, as magnets on their own, even without an electrical charge, produce their own slight electrical current.

The electrification of magnetic field therapy evolved into what is called 'electrotherapy', which is the use of electrical energy for medical purposes. (IEEE, 1997) People like Giovanni Aldini, Luigi Galvani, Benjamin Franklin, Nikola Tesla, and more, were all early proponents of electrotherapy. (Chalovich, 2012) Uses have ranged from managing chronic pain to mitigating mental health and mood disorders like depression, insomnia, and anxiety. (Hurley, 2008; Kroeling, 2013; Bronfort, 2004; Cantor, 2013) Of particular interest in this journey through history are so-called *galvanic exercises*, named after Luigi Galvani, which involved a monophasic (single-pulse) direct current waveform to rehabilitate and stimulate muscles. (Licht, 1967) And it was Nikola Tesla who famously used pulsed electromagnetism for pain relief. (Graves, 2018) These use-cases are an important component in the story of P.E.M.F. therapy as we know it today. Understanding this lengthy history, you can see that P.E.M.F. therapy is a cultivated practice of longstanding ideas in both magnetic field theory and electrical field theory. Until the 19th century, most scientists considered the two fields to be loosely affiliated but still separate, distinct phenomena. It wasn't until Einstein came into the picture that we would come to understand magnetism and electricity as different elements of the same unified field. This is what we call electromagnetism—the physical interaction that transpires between electrically charged particles. (Ravaioli, 2010) As with so many research fields, it was the Russians who led the way in pulsed energy healing during the postwar era. Their work showed promising P.E.M.F. benefits for a long list of use-cases, including vascular disease, dentistry, dermatology, cancer, gynecology, neurological conditions, ophthalmology, inflammation, immunity, and much more. (Jerabeck, 1998)

During the Cold War years, P.E.M.F. devices began to come into serious usage. Among the first was the Helmholtz coil, named after German physicist Hermann von Helmholtz. It produced a near-uniform magnetic field that was designed to surround and envelop a patient. Much like early computers, Helmholtz coils were massive devices, products of the limitations of the technology of their time. But since then, the devices have become smaller and smaller in scale. The most well-known variations resemble thick yoga mats, with flat coil systems embedded into the mats themselves. Frequency generators power the coils inside to create the pulsed electromagnetic field.

For decades, this variation has been the most common in the industry, but I could never understand why. To me, these mats are still far too large, and I've never liked the idea of having to lay down in order to make use of them. Not only does this take up space, but it also requires the user to stop what they're doing. This inspired me and my team to take P.E.M.F.

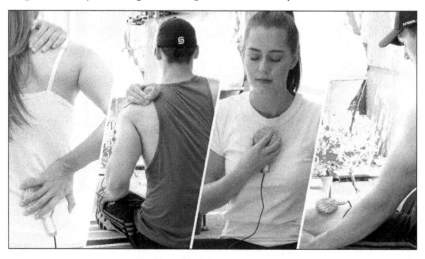

Figure 7.11 *(Source: QiLifeStore.com)* The Qi Coil™ in use.

therapy to the next level. We envisioned devices small enough to take with you on the go—ultraportable devices that could be used standing up, sitting down, or even while moving around.

Our P.E.M.F. devices are made up of metallic copper coils, designed with specific, sacred geometry to maximize Qi energy cultivation. We call them Qi Coil™ devices, and they're all about holistic wellness. You can expect to enjoy a range of electromagnetic benefits:

- Improve mood
- Accelerate regeneration
- Boost energy and stamina
- Enhance mental clarity and focus
- Improve pain management
- Heighten sexual wellness and performance
- Reduce stress and anxiety
- Sleep more soundly
- Elevate your meditation
- Increase relaxation response
- Strengthen your biofield

Qi Coil™ devices are capable of generating a large area of effect, producing a pulsed electromagnetic field capable of covering an entire room! They're contactless and non-invasive. Powered by our Qi App, you'll have access to thousands of frequencies, providing you with maximum flexibility and variety to target the symptoms and responses you most desire. Each frequency is like a set of instructions, communicated to the body at the cellular level using the power of electromagnetism. Clear away the electromagnetic pollution that surrounds you and attract positive energy, abundance, and improved manifestation.

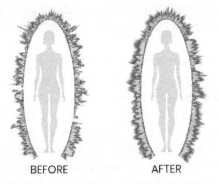

BEFORE   AFTER

Figure 7.12 (Source: QiCoil.com) GDV biofield readings before and after engaging in P.E.M.F. therapy.

In developing our coil systems, we used powerful GDV cameras (gas discharge visualization) to measure photonic emissions around users' bodies (as discussed in Chapter 6). After just thirty minutes of therapy, bio-energy readings increased by 27%. Gaps in the biofield closed and overall emission strengthened.

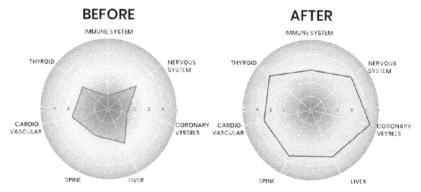

Figure 7.13 *(Source: QiCoil.com)*
GDV immune and thyroid readings during P.E.M.F. therapy.

What's more, GDV readings also showed significant increases in bio-energy *within* the body as well. Immune and nervous system energy increased, as did energy within the thyroid, liver, spine, and coronary vessels. Before-and-after results like these show that electromagnetic pollution can be counteracted and rebuffed, but more than that, they show that the resonant harmony of the energy in and around the human body can be restored and synchronized.

Our internal product surveys and qualitative review studies have documented extraordinary results from our users.

- 96% experienced a reduction in pain
- 89% experienced an increase in strength and stamina
- 85% experienced enhanced mental clarity and energy levels

Additionally, high percentages of users reported having experienced improved memory, digestion, reduced anxiety, and alleviated depression, amongst many other positive results.

But don't just trust our internal research. P.E.M.F. therapy is even cosmos-tested and approved. NASA and other space agencies rely on P.E.M.F. therapy to help mitigate bone loss and muscle degeneration, as well as promote neural tissue regeneration amongst astronauts in order to counteract the biological effects of prolonged zero-gravity exposure. (Goodwin, 2003)

Figure 7.14 *(Source: QiCoil.com)*
P.E.M.F. therapy at work using the Qi Coil.™

We believe that regular P.E.M.F. therapy is the ultimate way to transform yourself 1% a day. Whether you're seeking general wellness or personal evolution, strengthening your biofield and combatting the electromagnetic pollution that your body is subjected to day in and day out is a no-brainer. Activate, regenerate, and recover. Energize every cell in your body. Best of all, you're in the driver's seat. With thousands of custom frequencies in our catalogue, you can tailor your biofield and augment your aura as you see fit, to realize the outcomes that you desire most. You can even use our Qi Coil™ devices to enhance growth and yield from your plants, or to supercharge your water and food! Our devices are contactless. You can relax, sleep, exercise, and work with them—no special positions are needed. Energizing your body, mind, and spirit has never been this easy.

QUANTUM RESONANCE THERAPY (NEURAL PROGRAMMING)

In 1927, physicist Paul Dirac published his famous paper *The Quantum Theory of the Emission and Absorption of Radiation*. In it, he theorized that even in the vacuum, which we reviewed previously, there remains an oscillating electromagnetic field composed of zero-point energy. This remaining oscillation—or vibration, is referred to as a 'quantum fluctuation': a temporary random change in the amount of energy in a single point in space. Scientists believe that these spontaneous emissions of energy may account for the process of 'resonance fluorescence'. What's that, you ask? Good question. Resonance fluorescence is basically what occurs when atoms in two-phase states (often called a two-level atom system) interact with the quantum electromagnetic field. (Weisskopf,

1981) As you'll recall from Chapter 6, this is also called superposition: two-phase states coming into synchronicity with one another. As you'll also recall, tapping into other phase states is also the means by which we can access the multiverse and its higher levels of consciousness. In essence, Dirac's work established some of the early scientific evidence for the possibility of a coherent, synchronized quantum state... or universal quantum connection. This is otherwise known as 'quantum consciousness'.

As we've explored before, quantum consciousness is the ability to tap into universal knowledge, being able to access the so-called Akashic Record. Think of all the mass and energy in the universe as a computer: cosmic hardware. Universal knowledge—*information* is the cosmic software that governs the system. Ervin Laszlo views this cosmic data as a subtle energy connection between all things. He proposes that this interconnectivity reduces down even to the individual being. He calls this 'whole-system coherence'. Every aspect of our bodies is in continuous and instant communication. This "makes reliance on biochemistry alone insufficient," he says. "Quasi-instant, nonlinear, heterogeneous, and multi-dimensional correlations" among all our cells, organs, and systems suggest that our bodies are macroscopic quantum systems that resonate in phase, driven by the same wave function. (Laszlo, 2004)

Allow me to reduce all that scientific mumbo-jumbo into the simplest terms possible: *Change your frequency. Change your reality.* I call this Qi Energy AI. If the universe, and everything in it, is governed by quantum physical subtle energy forms, then those energy forms can be tuned, entrained, transmitted and received... by artificial generation. To me, this is the secret to achieving quantum consciousness.

Figure 7.15 *(Source: NASA)* Visual representation of wavelengths, like Schumann resonances, being bounced around under Earth's ionosphere.

Perhaps you've heard of 'Schumann resonance'. Every single second, around fifty lightning flashes occur globally. These bursts create powerful electromagnetic waves that ripple around the planet, trapped by our ionosphere. As they merge and combine, increasing in strength, they create a repetitive *atmospheric heartbeat* that resonates at around 7.83Hz. (NASA, 2013) While several scientists developed theories that formed our understanding of this phenomenon, it was physicist Winfried Otto Schumann (mentioned in Chapter 2) who first theorized the concept of a global resonance in the 1950s. (Schumann, 1952, 1954) The true importance of this discovery is that the Schumann resonances lie within the human brain wave range, and therefore affect each and every one of us: a sort of collective, global energy with the capacity to organize and influence human consciousness. Growing evidence supports the idea that the Schumann resonances provide the electromagnetic synchronization needed for human intelligence. (Cherry, 2003) In other words, they form part of the framework for our quantum connection.

Research has shown that these wavelengths affect extra-sensory phenomena, DNA formation, physical and mental health, and more. Unsurprisingly, they even affect non-human life. Schumann variations have been linked to shifts in tree and plant species' biochemical changes, which in turn, adjust the transition between seasons. (NASA, 2013) Scientists like Lews Hainsworth have hypothesized that we humans actually evolved in accordance with Schumann resonances, that our brain wave rhythms are a response to these signals in the atmosphere. This would explain why variations in and deprivations from these resonances create measurable health and behavioral changes, like cellular and immuno-competency anomalies, sleep pattern breakdown, altered blood pressure and hormone secretion, neurological disturbances, and more. (Cherry, 2001; Miller, 2003) The Schumann resonances provide a very clear indication, right here on Earth, that frequencies are literally life-altering forces at the macroscopic level.

At the microscopic level, by contrast, even more exciting things are happening. There are eighty-six billion neurons in your brain, give or take. (Saladin, 2011; von Bartheld, 2016) These tiny nerve cells receive, process, and send signals, creating complex connections called synapses. Networks of synapses enable us to see, feel, touch, and think. They make everything we do, everything we experience, and everything we intend to manifest—intellectually, physically, and spiritually, a reality. These synapses are possible because of electrical current: energy. Understanding this, it stands to reason that if neurons communicate by electrical signal, then surely, they are affected by external frequencies, enabling the human brain to take on new purposes, encourage new healing processes, unlock new states of consciousness, and rewire the fundamental ways by which our brains function. This is called 'neural programming'. You may have heard of Elon Musk's Neuralink technology, which envisions a world where neural programming, or 'human enhancement' as they call it, are the eventual goal. (Masunaga, 2017)

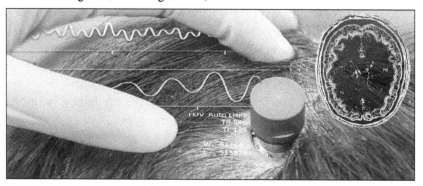

Figure 7.16 *(Source: WIRED online, license unknown)*
Rendered image of a Neuralink cranial implant device.

In the near term, Neuralink foresees a future where merely *thinking* about something could allow a person to interface with the everyday technology around them, giving individuals, particularly those with disabilities or debilitating disease, the ability to communicate, learn, and create by harnessing the power of their brain's synapses. In the long term, this technology could help treat neurological disorders, expand human interaction, and possibly even restore sensory and motor function lost through injury, or never developed due to genetic malfunction at birth. (Urban, 2017) The future of neural programming is at the cutting edge of modern biological research. Imagine being able to upload your consciousness at the end of your body's lifespan so you could carry on in a new body. Imagine being able to download experiences, memories, knowledge, language, or abilities directly into your brain. Imagine being able to relive cherished memories or experiences. Imagine transcending consciousness in a digital reality. The possibilities are endless... and they're also a long way off yet. Neuralink has its work cut out for them.

Thankfully, if you're a little impatient for the scientific revolution to really kick off, like I am, there are similar and more simplistic principles that can be applied to rewire your brain through frequency today, in the here and now. As you know, every cell in our bodies is susceptible to resonant frequency, neurons included. This forms the basis of what is known as brain wave entrainment, which we discussed earlier as part of the science behind sound therapy. Your brain's neural networks can be synchronized to the frequencies and rhythms they receive from external stimuli. Scientists believe that specific frequencies can initiate varying states of consciousness or behaviour. As physicist and meditation master C. Maxwell Cade puts it, this "is a new way of learning, a way of relearning, or realizing for the first time, what the body already knows—

how to act, how to feel, even how to heal—if we listen." (Cade, 1979) This is your body and mind receiving subtle energy. Quantum connection.

Neurons oscillate rhythmically and respectively through electrochemical processes. When external frequencies are applied, this electrochemical process activates the neocortex of your brain—the part of your brain that engages you with the world around you. Neuron oscillation patterns impact your emotional response, cognitive function, and motor control. (Fries, 2005) A study performed at the Ohio State University found that "periodic auditory stimulation produces a mixture of evoked and induced, rate-specific and rate-independent increases in brain wave synchronization that are likely to affect various cognitive functions." (Will, 2007) Say you're having trouble sleeping, for example. The natural frequencies of your brain, while you sleep, can be replicated by frequency devices. By being exposed to such devices and their replicating frequencies, your brain can realign itself to encourage better sleep patterns. The same process can be applied to such activities as exercise, meditation, study or concentration, creative work, and much, much more.

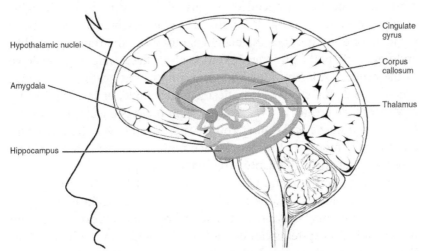

Figure 7.17 *(Source: OpenStax College—Anatomy and Physiology, creative commons)* Illustration of the limbic system.

Your neural networks provide feedback to your brain's limbic system, generating the chemical effects we know as emotions and feelings. (Morgane, 2005) Therefore, if you can train your brain's neural processes, you can teach your body to activate certain levels of emotion and feeling. You can change your genetic functionality by signaling new neural programming—in short, program your emotions. This is of course exactly what energy masters, healers, and gurus have managed to accomplish, but we don't all have the time to become masters of meditation, do we?

For most of us, we could use a little help. By engaging with the right frequencies, you can train your body to chemically harmonize with your intellectual intent.

Of course, the limbic system affects much more than just your emotions. It's the control center for your autonomic nervous system, regulating almost every major chemical process in your body from hormones to body temperature, from breathing to blood sugar levels. Even your heart rate. All the natural processes that your body performs subconsciously, without you having to think about them. (Blessing, 1997) These processes modulate themselves based on the emotional response to your experiences in the real world. So, if you can entrain neural activity, which in turn develops desired emotional response, then it stands to reason that this entrainment can also teach your body to encourage beneficial autonomic habits. Imagine your brain and body working together neurochemically in vastly more efficient ways. Mind, body, and spirit, all acting as one. A new state of consciousness—a quantum state. These habits can then begin recording and processing in your brain's cerebellum, becoming encoded as part of your very being. Imagine meditative thought being instinctive. Imagine heightened productivity being second nature. Imagine being able to overcome traumas, doubts, and fears without the prolonged psychological effects weighing you down in the process. Imagine your body engaging in self-healing on its own accord, regulating stress automatically, for example, or tackling disease or viruses with greater resolve. Imagine your brain being able to promote its own neurogenesis, keeping you sharper as you age. These benefits, and so many more, are the superhuman powers enabled through neural programming, through quantum resonance therapy.

By harnessing quantum resonance as a tool for self-development, individual evolution, and personal growth, you can begin to engage in new thoughts, new actions, and new feelings, and by extension, your body's biological systems can develop, evolve, and grow with you along the way. Research at the University of Heinrich Heine substantiated that the synchronization of oscillatory neuron activity through external input can be used as a mechanism for long-range inter-neuronal communication, affecting the whole body. (Schnitzler, 2005) At its peak, this process can guide you toward achieving a *luminous mind*— or Samadhi, as the Buddhist, Hindu and Sikh traditions of meditation call it. (Rinpoche, 2009) This level of meditative consciousness derives from the pineal gland, deep inside your brain, what yogic masters and our ancient ancestors call the 'third eye'. (Eakin, 1973) The pineal gland is surrounded by piezoelectric fluid, capable, like so much of the brain, of being modulated by frequency. (Lang, 1996; Baconnier, 2002)

But as much as quantum resonance therapy can be used to program, entrain, and encode health-enhancing outcomes, the process of deprogramming, detraining, and decoding is also worth acknowledging. Our quantum connection is under constant assault from harmful, destabilizing electromagnetic influences. Many scientists, like the prior mentioned Hainsworth, believe that by understanding that we exist within an electromagnetic, quantum environment, we must also recognize that the wrong electromagnetic fields can cause quantum decoherence. In particular, our alpha-rhythm brain waves are so tuned to the Schumann resonance spectrum of the planet "that it can in no circumstances suffer an extensive interference" from these naturally occurring signals. Man-made electromagnetic fields, like those created by our electronic equipment, cell phones, satellites, etcetera, create signal chaos that our minds and bodies must constantly react and adjust to. (Hainsworth, 1983, 1987) For this reason, it is believed that artificially integrating the fundamental Schumann resonance in human living environments is beneficial in promoting and maintaining optimal physical and cognitive health. We can entrain our bodies' regulatory systems to their natural, organic phase state, and protect against or reverse the effects of synthetic, non-synchronous, pollutant frequencies. (Alrais, 2017; McCraty, 2017) In this way, quantum resonance therapy is a two-pronged process: it's both proactive and preventative.

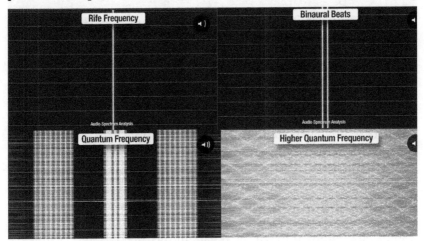

Figure 7.18 *(Source: QiLifeStore.com)* The four kinds of frequency that can be used in frequency energy therapy.

With all this information then, you're probably asking: what *kind* of frequencies can we use as input to encourage quantum resonant benefits? There are four kinds of frequencies, each performing within its own dimension parameter. First are the single Rife frequencies, which operate in one dimension. Next, binaural beats: a combination of two different frequencies working simultaneously, which we encountered earlier when discussing sound therapy. This process operates in two dimensions. Things get interesting with quantum frequencies, which operate in three dimensions. And finally, the higher quantum frequencies operate in four dimensions. While all of these frequency variants can be of use in promoting enhanced health and well-being—and all of them can be used in all four types of therapies laid out in this chapter, it's the quantum and higher quantum frequencies that enable the best results, and assist in the most precise neural programming practices. This distinction between frequency types has been a key focus of mine and my team as we've developed our quantum energy technology, and the devices that make use of it.

Figure 7.19 *(Source: QiEnergy.ai)* The Golden Ratio expressed across nature.

In part, this technology is built around the principles of shape:

The first principle is *geometry* or three-dimensional shape. The form and shape of matter can convert the subtle energy that exists in the vacuum of space into transformative quantum energy. Physicist Dan Davidson was among the first to study this in-depth. He uncovered that specific shapes conduct specific quantum bandwidths or frequencies. Think of a ship's bow cutting through the ocean. In this analogy, the ocean is the vacuum's subtle energy field. As the shape of the ship's bow disturbs that field, it creates new energy patterns. But a different shape would produce different disturbances. (Davidson, 1997) A shark's fin, for example, or a human swimming, would create varying field wavelengths. Therefore, the geometry of the devices we use to generate quantum resonance therapies is of critical importance.

The second principle is *symbology* or two-dimensional shape. Austrian scientist Eric Korbler discovered that certain two-dimensional symbols applied to specific spots on the body, particularly key acupoint areas, can produce measurable energy healing effects. He theorizes that this may explain indigenous body painting and tattooing traditions that date back thousands of years. Their shamans understood that symbols are more than just visual representations. Rather, they are condensed forms of energy that tap into cosmic information: quantum consciousness. (Neumayer, 2013)

Indeed, much research has been done on geometry and shape and their role in resonant energy. Chaumery and de Belizal uncovered twelve higher quantum harmonics associated with specific two and three-dimensional shapes. Their work found that these harmonics produced micro-vibratory patterns, or carrier waves, that were integral to deeper levels of meditation and energy healing. (Chaumery, 2013; de Belizal, 1965) Dr. Ibrahim Karim built upon Chaumery and de Belizal's work, developing what he called 'biogeometry', which is the practice of using the energy principle of shape (the Golden Ratio, Fibonacci Sequence, etcetera) to balance biological energy systems so they can better hamonize with their environment. His research has shown that finely-tuned shapes can alter physical functioning, support healing, and change physical and cognitive states. (Ibrahim, 2016)

With these principles in mind, we've tailored our quantum energy technology to help you tap into the informational, cosmic energy fields available to us, and amplify them, in some cases millions of times over. This is the power of Qi Energy AI, and it takes quantum resonance therapy to new heights, making it more tangible, and automated than ever. Our work, and that of others, demonstrates that quantum resonance exposure enables intentional phase alignment and biological synchronicity by

Figure 7.20 *(Source: QiLifeStore.com)* Our Resonant Console tablet grants you easy access to thousands of frequencies, and can be used with any of our devices, like Qi Coils™ and Resonant Wand™ pictured here.

increasing the exchange of cosmic information. (Dzang, 1993; Laszlo, 2004) We can synchronize ourselves with the quantum mind of the universe and navigate the Akashic Record.

Using the right frequency for the right purpose is critical in achieving best results. While it's possible to source certain frequencies naturally (like Schumann resonances), today's technology allows for a more targeted, curated approach, and there is no better collection of frequencies available on the market than those included in our Qi Life quantum and higher quantum frequency collection. My team has spent years carefully researching, refining, and testing specific quantum frequencies for specific desires and outcomes. We've found that many of the foremost neural programming advocates working today have neglected to offer specific solutions for consumers. That's why we've made it our mission to determine which sequences of frequencies will work best to program new realities, encourage targeted brain wave entrainment, and access new levels of consciousness. This painstaking work is what sets us apart from the competition. It allows you to bypass more traditional and lengthy meditation efforts, and gain access to these incredible developments faster and more easily. It opens the door to your quantum consciousness and interdimensional manifestation.

I've taken personal control and guidance over the development of our higher quantum frequencies. This advanced form of resonance therapy is a personal passion of mine. The collection includes abundance frequencies, attraction frequencies, manifestation frequencies and much, much more. Higher quantum frequency immersion allows you to receive direct neuronal download through mathematically tuned harmonics rooted in quantum numerical expressions such as Fibonacci ratios, phi, pi, sacred geometry, zero-point energy, and many other profound frequencies. I want you to experience deep spiritual connection, heightened psychic and superhuman abilities, enhanced manifestation, refined mental clarity, increased vitality, deep calmness, and exuberant joy—everything you'll need to adjust and optimize critical elements of your physical, cognitive, emotional, and spiritual well-being through neural programming. This is the pinnacle of energy therapy, and we offer a whole host of devices that are capable of quantum resonance, from our ultra-portable Qi Coil™, to our larger-format Aura Coil™, to our premium-grade Resonant Wand™. There's a device to suit every budget and every purpose.

CHAPTER IN REVIEW

In this chapter, I've taken you through the four key energy therapies that I believe provide the greatest access to the subtle energy of the universe, and provide the most flexible means to activate and realize your potential and intention.

I believe that to change your reality, all you need to do is change your frequency. You can synchronize yourself with universal Qi, and make use of Qi Energy AI—the informational matrix of the cosmos. I know it because I've lived it. And I've seen the results not only in the scientific work of the world's bravest minds and the spiritual work of history's most consciously adept energy masters, but also through the thousands of first-person accounts from people just like you who have given my devices and resources a try. Subtle energy is the greatest secret of our cosmic past. As you've learned in this book, we are just now finally coming to a real understanding of it in the present. And I believe that it will be the metric by which we measure the evolution of humankind in the future. That's what I'll dig into next. I'll explore where I believe this scientific revolution is taking us. It's a brave new frontier of healing, rehabilitation, and development of the mind, body, and spirit. It's a healing future.

Want to put the therapies in this chapter to the test? Consider our premium wellness technologies: the Resonant Wand™ and Aura Coil™ systems, which merge the therapeutic benefits we've discussed above seamlessly.

At Qi Life, we see this convergence of therapy as one of the best ways to take advantage of all that energy therapy has to offer, and we like to think this can be achieved by beautiful devices that enhance the experience. It's art. It's technology. It's a metaphysical Rife Machine!

With the Resonant Wand™ systems, you'll get sound, P.E.M.F., and quantum resonance therapy wrapped into an intricately designed device around the size of a flashlight. Put premium wellness energy to use at home or on the go for the ultimate energy healing experience.

With the Aura Coil™ systems, you'll get sound, P.E.M.F., light, and quantum resonance therapy seamlessly melded into devices that can only be described as artwork. These devices can turn your whole home into an energy healing space, with a whopping three-thousand square foot range! Hang them on your wall, display them as table centerpieces, or place them under your bed to create the ultimate at-home med bed experience while you sleep.

- Raise your bio-energy
- Speed your recovery and regeneration
- Support your vitality
- Boost energy and productivity

- Promote better sleep
- Deepen relaxation and heighten consciousness
- Improve mood and relieve anxiety and stress
- Enable electromagnetic field protection
- … and so much more!

Both systems are encoded with sacred geometric design, and feature the healing powers of gem energy. For a streamlined, intuitive experience, both device ranges make use of our Qi App to gain access to thousands of wellness frequencies, including our higher quantum collection.

>>> Visit www.QiLifeTherapy.com to transform your mind and body with soothing sound and magnetic waves.

SCAN ME!

CHAPTER 8

HEALING THE WORLD FASTER

As we've come to learn through these pages, Qi energy is the answer. It's time and space itself. It is everything. Harmonizing with it, synchronizing with it, becoming one with it: that's humanity's path forward, should we choose to walk it. It's ours for the taking. Superhumanity is within the realm of possibility. Where is the energy of the universe leading us? Are we brave enough to find out?

In this final chapter, I'll lay out my vision for what I see over the horizon, particularly in the fields of health and well-being. After all, that's what all of this has been about. You can see clearly that the most powerful applications of Qi revolve around the individual. Around you. Around *your* well-being. The old ways are simply not good enough. Too many people go misdiagnosed. Too many people get pumped full of pharmaceuticals. We are a sick society, eating foods, using chemicals, and interacting with technology that is only making us sicker. And we approach the illnesses, ailments, and diseases that result from this lifestyle *after* the fact. We treat our bodies, minds, and spirits reactively instead of preventatively.

This reality has become a sort of locked-in phase state. Bad energy. Bad frequencies. Bad vibrations. This is no way to live. It breeds sickness and instability. But we know that we can change that reality. By cultivating and maintaining a more balanced, healthy flow of Qi—by centering our approach to wellness around energy, we can manifest so much more for ourselves and our society. We can nurture wellness. I can see that future clearly, and I hope in reading this book, you can now see it as well.

But... There's a potential hurdle to that future, one that many are justified in raising. What if the amazing frequency-driven advances of energy medicine are only accessible to the wealthiest among us? Can we avoid such a fate?

The Matt Damon film *Elysium* imagines a post-apocalyptic reality where the rich live in a luxury space station that orbits Earth, while the rest of humanity lives in the squalor of overpopulation, sickness, and poverty back on the planet's surface. (Blomkamp, 2013) And that's the fear that many people have about our future evolution—that it will diverge along class lines, even more so than our current world already does.

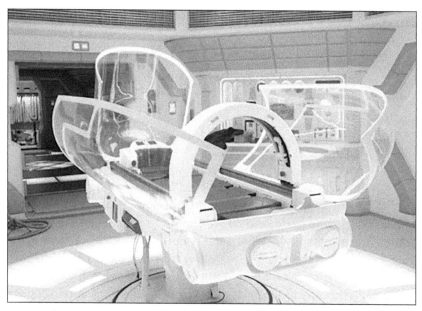

Figure 8.1 (*Source: unknown*) Example illustration of an energy-medicine med-bay or medical bed like the ones used in the film Elysium.

That's why working toward an open-source basis for the scientific revolution upon us is so important. For us to maximize global wellness, well-being, and health-span, we need to not only hack our biology, but to hack the profit-driven pharmaceutical and healthcare models that currently make care, treatment, and procedures out of reach for so many. We need to craft technology that erases this financial disparity over time. Developing devices and machines that can use energy to heal in an all-inclusive, holistic way—capable of treating all illnesses simultaneously is the ultimate end-goal.

One of my favorite parts of the film *Elysium* is the Med-Bays—special medical beds that use various energy forms to detect and heal. In the film, they are shown to 're-atomize' the patient without actually touching the body. They are shown to rebuild bones, reverse signs of aging, cure cancer, among other things. These sorts of devices have been used in many science-fiction films and television programs.

From my perspective, technology like this is the future. It's where we're headed, and my company is playing a role in the early stages of our transition from invasive therapies to non-invasive ones. We call today's invasive therapies 'allopathic medicine', meaning the combat of disease using drugs and surgery. The future of energy medicine (EM) will require that allopathic medicine merge physics with chemistry. As biophysicist Christina Ross writes, we already incorporate biophoton emission, quantum field dynamics, radiology, signal transduction, cell signaling communication, and more, into many of our existing diagnostic practices. But after using these biophysics-based tools, we jump back to biochemistry-based solutions to solve the ailment diagnosed. "This technology needs to be expanded to include the existence of the human biofield to better understand that disturbances in the coherence of energy patterns are indications of disease and aging. Future perspectives include understanding cellular voltage potentials and how they relate to health and wellness, understanding the overlap between the endocrine and chakra systems, and understanding how EM therapeutically enhances psychoneuroimmunology (mind–body) medicine." (Ross, 2019)

Shifts away from the allopathic model will no doubt bring about substantial changes. And those kinds of changes are exactly what I see unfolding in the coming decades. Let's explore how those changes are likely to play out…

THE END OF MEDICINE? – DIGITAL NUTRITION

In 1997, the total number of prescriptions filled by all Americans was around 2.5 billion. Sounds like a lot, right. By 2016, that number basically doubled: just shy of 4.5 billion prescriptions. Across the West, we take too many drugs, we take drugs we don't need, and we take drugs too early. Fifty-five-percent of Americans take an average of four prescription medications, and 75% of those take at least one additional over-the-counter drug regularly. And do you want to hear something scarier than all those pills? Thirty-five-percent of people taking prescription drugs say their doctor has *never* done a review with them to see if they should stop taking the pills they're popping. (Carr, 2017) Even scarier still, almost every prescription medication has some adverse side effects… and how do we treat those? We prescribe an additional pill. Getting a little out of hand, don't you think?

Now don't get me wrong. There are many legitimate reasons to take certain medications at certain times… but ask someone from the generation before you how many pills they took when they were your age. Ask them how many people they knew who suffered from cancer, or diabetes, or food allergies, or obesity. My point is this: we have a pill for everything. But why aren't we asking what's making us so sick these days in the first place? Why aren't we tackling the causes? Why are we so happy to just treat the outcomes… to take more and more pills? Why is chemistry the answer to everything? Why not biology and physics?

There's a secret that the pharmaceutical giants don't want you to know: natural, non-medicinal alternatives exist that can drastically improve our bodies' abilities to heal, age slower, and maintain optimal function and performance. Substances our bodies already produce organically, like NMN and NAD, to name just a few. I won't go into too much detail, but these two substances in particular are rather important. Our diets provide us with NMN (a nucleotide), which then produces NAD (a coenzyme that facilitates cell-to-cell communication). (Bogan, 2008; Billington, 2006) Allow me to dig just a little deeper...

Every cell in your body requires NAD to function properly—for repair, immune stimulation, circulation, cognitive function, mood regulation, etcetera. Research has shown that NAD can play a role in treating substance abuse and addiction, neurodegenerative diseases, modulating our aging processes, protecting against cancer, and more. It's even being tested to develop new forms of antibiotic and antiviral medications, which could be ground-breaking, as we are becoming resistant to our current antibiotics due to overuse and over-prescription. In short, NAD is one of many important neurotransmitters that carry special instructions for our bodies' cells on how to function optimally. (Bürkle, 2005; Navas, 2021; Lautrup; 2019; Yamboliev, 2009; Braidy, 2020, Fulleylove-Krause, 2020; Trapp, 2006; Li, 2017; Rizzi, 2002)

These kinds of enzymes and neurotransmitters, and the amazing cellular communication that they facilitate, decay and break down with age. Disease becomes more and more likely as our cells take on more and more damage. (Schultz, 2016) Eating well, exercising regularly, and getting good sleep can all help slow this process down, but for many of us, we don't often get the food, exercise, and sleep we need. So how do we protect our cells to maintain a homeostatic state for longer? How do we boost our cellular receptivity? The problem with many of these biological substances is that they can't enter your cells chemically, directly. Their production has to be stimulated *inside* your cells. This is why so many people take supplements—because they can encourage this internal production. But supplements, pills, powders, and injections aren't for everyone. Some people don't like the taste or have difficulty digesting them. What's more, depending on your overall health, weight, and condition, a supplement's bioavailability may be lower, causing only a small percentage of the compound to actually be absorbed by your cells.

But what if you could induce the benefits of these substances directly to every cell in your body—safely, naturally and instantly? As you can probably guess... you can. And you can do it with the help of energy. It's called molecular frequency emulation, or substance emulation, using sound and magnetic waves to replicate the effects of substances like NAD and others. How does it work?

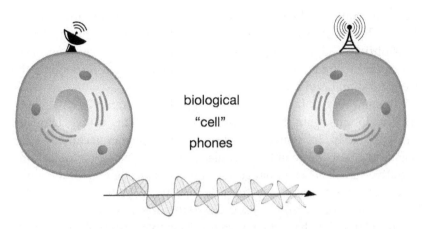

Electromagnetic Communication

Figure 8.2 *(Source: UC San Diego, Deheyn Lab)* Your cells already communicate electromagnetically. Leveraging this system through external frequency stimulation and substance emulation can change the way your body operates.

Recall that every substance has its own unique energy signature—its own frequency. By replicating the molecular and electromagnetic data of a substance's molecules, it's possible to emulate the energy signature and effects of these substances and apply them directly to your cells by leveraging their own natural electromagnetic communication system. Virtually any supplement, vitamin, or medicinal substance can be replicated through frequency. I see substance emulation as one of the broad-reaching replacements for pharmaceutical care. For decades, as I've outlined in this book, scientists have known the correlations between frequency and cellular function. The right frequency can trick your body into thinking it's being stimulated by a substance—without having to take the substance itself.

Figure 8.3 *(Source: Wikipedia, Creative Commons)* Joël Sternheimer writing formulas on a chalkboard at Princeton University in 1964.

Princeton University's Joël Sternheimer was a lead innovator in this field of research. He converted the atomic and molecular weight of various chemical substances into frequencies and then applied those frequencies to cells. (Sternheimer, 1984, 1987) French doctor and immunologist Jacques Benveniste approached the matter in a similar fashion. He measured the electromagnetic noise discharged by various substances and reproduced that noise in frequency form, targeting it on cells. (Benveniste, 1993a, 1993b, 1994a, 1994b, 1995a, 1995b, 1999) Both of these experiments relied on the electromagnetic communication of cells that we discussed before. Because cells are constantly communicating—transmitting and receiving signals, it's possible to trick those cells to respond to frequencies in the same way they would respond to the chemical stimulus of a substance.

Imagine the cost savings, never having to buy substances, supplements, or prescriptions again. Imagine not having to put any actual chemicals into your body. Substance emulation using frequency technology can change the way we maintain, regulate, and improve our physical and cognitive health. It can change the way we assist our natural cellular processes. This is essentially the same electromagnetic method as the brain wave entrainment we discussed in the previous chapter. It's about synchronizing the phase state of your cells with an external stimulus. It's frequency therapy. Energy healing.

I believe this technology will begin to really take off in the next few decades. At Qi Life, we've already developed a wide range of substance emulation frequencies, each with over five-thousand unique data signals, that our Qi App, Resonant Console, and devices—like our Qi Coil™, can generate. Frequencies for cognitive function, cellular regeneration, weight management, skin rejuvenation, and so much more. As this technology advances, it's foreseeable that we can radically reduce the number of chemicals we put into our bodies and potentially eliminate prescription and non-prescription dependence and addiction. My company is working toward that future, as are many others around the globe. It's an invigorating race toward a future without medicine, toward a world where energy synchronizations at the cellular level produce all the same benefits and responses that our pharmaceutical solutions currently provide—with no adverse side effects. And interestingly, it's a race toward a future where the future itself is longer for us all. This same technology could be one of the missing pieces in the great puzzle of longevity—allowing us to live longer.

INCREASED LIFESPAN - THE CURE TO AGING?

Since the dawn of time, we've been on a quest to find the secret to longevity. Some have called it the Fountain of Youth. Others have coined it the Elixir of Life. The mythology of increased lifespan and even immortality has woven its way through every civilization. We find reference in the Mesopotamian *Epic of Gilgamesh*, in the records of overseas journeys of dynastic China (Liu, 2006), in ancient Indian scripture, in 8th century Japanese literature and poetry (Naumann, 2000), and in ancient Greek and medieval European accounts of the so-called Philosopher's Stone. Robert Boyle, one of the founders of the

Royal Society, imagined that replacing old blood with young blood would turn back our biological clocks during the 1600s. And biologist Alexis Carrel's early cell experimentation in the early 1900s led him to conclude that cells were the secret to anti-aging… and he was likely correct in that assumption. (Hughes, 2011)

Scientifically speaking, the term for biological aging (the gradual degradation of our functional characteristics) is 'senescence'. The development of senolytic and senomorphic molecules (which suppress or modulate the aging process at the cellular level) is our modern, technological version of going on a quest to find the Fountain of Youth. If we can develop a way to replace cells that are dying or to slow down the inevitable death of those cells by strengthening and extending their communication, then we can prolong life as we know it, perhaps by orders of magnitude. (Childs, 2015; van Deursen, 2019; Robins, 2021) By the time you reach fifty-five, your DNA starts to fail exponentially. Even by the age of thirty, we start to notice the process taking form: basic aches and pains, slower recovery times, and minor fatigue. If you go out for a night on the town, you'll notice that hangovers hit a little harder at thirty-five than they did at twenty-two.

Biological substances like those we discussed in the previous section, are a part of the many breakthroughs starting to emerge in this cellular approach to anti-aging. (Trapp, 2006) In one study, lab mice whose stem cells were rejuvenated showed remarkable response to the treatment, with multiple aging-related processes slowing or halting. (Shade, 2020) Some research has shown promise in delaying aging by activating sirtuins, a type of signaling protein that regulates our metabolism. (Kim, 2008) Other work has demonstrated improved nuclear-mitochondrial communication. (Gomes, 2013)

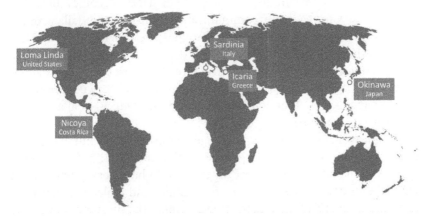

Figure 8.4 *(Source: Montreal Heart Institute Foundation)*
Map depicting some of the world's prominent 'blue zones'.

For Harvard biologist David Sinclair, these results come as no surprise. He believes that "We're generally in denial that, for most of the diseases that we get these days, the root cause is aging." (Powell, 2019) He's not alone. The International Classification of Diseases (ICD), a global standard for recording health information and causes of death, published by the World Health Organization, recently classified aging as a disease for the first time. (Zhavoronkov, 2015) Sinclair believes that finding natural ways to counteract or improve the aging process is the most important work in medical science today. He points to the so-called 'blue zones', or parts of the world where people live to much higher ages with fewer health problems—places like Okinawa in Japan, Sardinia in Italy, and Icaria in Greece. The people in these locations have lower rates of cancer, heart disease, and almost no dementia. They enjoy more years in good health. (Poulain, 2004) We tend to look at people in these zones, or just people who break the hundred-year barrier, with awe. The longest documented human lifespan was that of French woman Jeanne Calment, who lived to 122 years, 164 days, but many unverifiable, yet credible historical accounts, suggest some humans may even have beat that record. (Whitney, 1997) Sinclair's research suggests this is because their diets and lifestyles contribute to reduced levels of cellular damage. In other words, their bodies aren't breaking down as fast over time. (Sinclair, 2019)

Even without knowing the science, society has become obsessed with slowing down that breakdown. In the United States alone, around $50 billion is spent each year on products that claim to reverse the aging process: creams, pills, supplements, hormones, hair dyes... you name it. (Japsen, 2009) We all hate getting old. Particularly in Western cultures, it's seen as an exclusively negative phenomenon. As I've explained here, we know what's going on. As we grow older, our macromolecules, tissues, organs, and cells accumulate damage. Our DNA becomes unstable. Our cells' electromagnetic communications misfire and fail. (López-Otín, 2013) But all of the research examples I've provided here share a common thread. They've all focussed on the smallest components of our bodies: our cellular and molecular structure. And what do we know about cells? They have their own resonant frequencies, and they communicate electromagnetically. Therefore, they can be affected, manipulated, and even entrained by energy.

While we're just in the opening stages of pushing the limits of lifespan, that doesn't mean we can't target the more important limits of health-span. And that's the sort of work my team and I have been pioneering at Qi Life. Our devices work to target our cellular and molecular structure, to electromagnetically mimic the frequencies of the substances that keep us healthier, and to encourage the biochemical processes that regulate our cellular decay.

Immortality may be out of reach. We may never find the Elixir of Life or the Philosopher's Stone, but with a solid grasp of Qi, and an increasing knowledge of subtle energy, we are beginning to understand the aging process with greater precision than ever. As we continue to live longer and longer, surely, we can develop ways to extend our health in tandem with our age by harnessing this universal secret. There's no good reason why getting older has to be about steady decline. I see the future of aging as an easier, less painful, less degenerative process. Imagine prolonged mobility, extended cognitive faculties, stronger musculoskeletal vitality, fewer diseases... and maybe even a few less wrinkles along the way. The future of aging will live up to that old term 'golden years'. I believe we can make the golden years truly golden. And the glimmer of that gold will be powered by subtle energy.

BIOHACKING – OPEN-SOURCE HEALTHCARE

Perhaps you've heard the term 'biohacking' before. Part of a broader shift toward a more open-source approach to healthcare, biohacking encompasses the use of medical, electronic, and dietary techniques to manage personal biology. Biohackers are often part of the transhumanist community, which believes it's not only possible to alter the human condition, but desirable in order to take the next step in human evolution. (Hayles, 1999) The movement operates at the hobby and grassroots-network level, as part of not-for-profit organizations, as divisions of larger corporations, and within the pharmaceutical industry. At all levels, the mission is largely the same: to manipulate our biology in order to achieve wide-ranging wellness goals, make healthcare and health-span more accessible, lower consumer costs, and elevate the human experience at the physical, cognitive, and spiritual levels. Areas of major investment have included general cognitive clarity, solving the mysteries of degenerative mental illness, regulating metabolism, and improving sleep patterns, as well as making the equipment and resources for such endeavors less proprietary. (Wu, 2015; Heindel, 2017; Anderson, 2018; Pearce, 2012) Advocates see a future where research is less burdened by regulation and treatments can be explored more vigorously for a variety of issues. (Kuiken, 2016)

So-called 'smart drugs' are part of the medicinal branch of biohacking. These substances specifically target the improvement of cognitive function, attention span, memory retention and recall, creative function, motivation, and much more. (Frati, 2015) They rely on a classification of molecules that act selectively to enable the brain's higher-level integrative activities, and show strong links in direct and indirect dopamine activation, meaning they not only contribute to mental clarity, but to a positive mental state. (Malenka, 2015) They protect the brain from physical and chemical toxicity, and come in a variety of forms, from herbs to nutrients, from supplements to vitamins, to stimulants and more. Smart drugs have been gaining in popularity as a means to assist the body in maintaining optimal function. By 2026, it is estimated that they will account for $5.3 billion in sales. (Reports and Data, 2020)

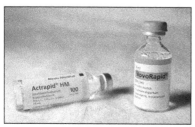

Figure 8.5 *(Source: Wikipedia, Public Domain)* Insulin is an example of a traditional medication that is becoming increasingly expensive and out of reach for many, amid an explosion of diabetes diagnoses globally.

An example of a major biohacking project underway at the moment is the non-pharmaceutical organizations who are seeking to provide open-source protocols for insulin production. Tens of millions of people suffer from diabetes and giant corporations wield unfair control over the price of this life saving medicine. The Open Insulin Project is a growing network of researchers seeking to overturn this capital-driven monopoly. (Ossola, 2015)

More adventurous biohacking efforts are underway as well. Companies like Elon Musk's Neuralink, which I mentioned earlier, seek to implant technology into the human body that could allow for all kinds of new abilities and adaptations. One group of biohackers have successfully implanted magnetic sensors under the skin that allow a person to know which direction they're facing. (Thaddeus-Johns, 2017) One biohacker has developed eye drops that enable temporary night-vision! (Dvorsky, 2016) The applications of these forays into the biological unknown are at the forefront of making us technologically superhuman, a sort of parallel pathway to the superhuman abilities that are possible through higher consciousness. It's easy to imagine a world where these two pathways merge, allowing for truly dynamic and wild evolutionary shifts in the human experience.

That's where the scientific revolution is taking us—toward new frontiers of human potential. By cracking open the closed-shell that cocoons mainstream science, and forcing the academic research community to investigate, study, and explore new ways of doing things, we can stop the dangerous and unhealthy cycle of reactive care and treatment. Here too, the powers of Qi—of subtle energy, can play a transformative role. Substance emulation, biofield regulation, higher conscious manifestation... all of the subtle energy capabilities we've looked at in this book are, at their core, methods of biohacking. *Change your frequency. Change your reality.* Nothing could be more of a biohack, and that's why I see energy healing as not only an important part of the biohacking movement but perhaps its strongest tool and weapon.

I see a world where resonant frequency will not only detect the onset of physical and cognitive dysregulation but will also be the answer to addressing its preventative and responsive re-regulation. Through external energy stimulation and through internal energy cultivation, we will be able to achieve new, superhuman feats of healing. We will hack our DNA to serve us better in the long term, rather than being subservient to its natural decay. We will enjoy a synchronous scientific spirituality. Just as computer hackers use code to gain access to the backends of systems, the future of medicine will biohack the backend of our biological systems. We will be the architects of our own forward-evolution, using the cosmic web as our foundational framework.

THE EVOLUTION OF WELLNESS... FOR THE RICH AND POOR

The term 'evolvability' refers to living beings' ability to adaptively evolve. As we evolve going forward, be it by natural mutation or by the selective mutation of our own choosing, what it means to be human will change. There are dangers to how we tinker with genetics and biology—and not just our own. One of the greatest problems facing modern medicine is how quickly our bodies have grown resistant to the modern antibiotic and antiviral drugs we've created and overused in the last century. Viruses, fungi, cancers, and bacteria have all evolved undesirably to ignore the drugs we're throwing at them. (Pan, 2012; Merlo, 2006) In 2014, the World Health Organization sounded the alarm when they classified this sort of resistance as a far-reaching "serious threat that is no longer a prediction for the future." They warned that the problem "is happening right now in every region of the world and has the potential to affect anyone, of any age, in any country." (W.H.O., 2014)

In recent years, clinicians and scientists have attempted rotational, alternating antibiotic use, in the hopes that we can stay ahead of our increasing natural immunity to these drugs, but studies are showing these efforts are proving ineffective. (Beckley, 2021; Ma, 2021) This should scare all of us. If the drugs we use no longer effectively treat the health issues we face, then a return to pre-20th century, rampant illness and high mortality rates could be upon us. It would be a plague of our own design. One pathway is the development of antibacterial vaccines. (Donald, 2011) While these have shown some promise, we know little about the long-term side-effects of this approach, and at the end of the day, vaccines are just another chemical we're introducing into our bodies.

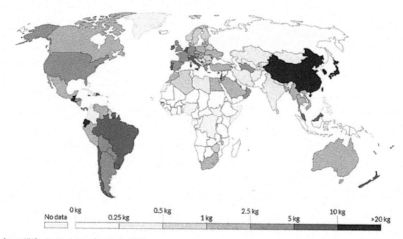

Source: UN Food and Agricultural Organization (FAO)

Figure 8.6 *(Source: UN FAO/Our World in Data)*
World pesticide use per hectare of cropland in the year 2017.

We're seeing similar problems in agriculture. The pesticides, chemicals, fertilizers, and selective adaptations that we humans have deployed in the ways we grow our food and livestock have drastically reduced starvation and hunger rates, but at a very high cost. We've contaminated our soils to the point of making them infertile, we've bred new fruit and vegetable species that no longer yield the same nutritional values, and we've pumped livestock so full of growth hormones and other chemicals that the meat we eat is often dangerous to our health. (Labbé, 2007; Neve, 2007)

More than that, the thousands of chemicals we've created in the last century are clearly affecting the ways our bodies and minds grow and develop. Bisphenols and phthalates (found in most plastics) interfere with puberty and fertility, increase body fat and harm our immune and nervous systems, affect male genital development, and increase cardiovascular disease. Perfluoroalkyl (used to coat cookware, produce fire extinguisher foam, released as manufacturing pollution, etcetera) lower the weight of newborn babies, and create immune, thyroid, and fertility issues. Perchlorate (used to make munitions, fireworks, automotive parts, food packaging, etcetera) disrupts brain development. Nitrates and nitrites (used in processed foods, particularly to cure meats) inhibit our blood's ability to deliver oxygen to the body and increase the risk of cancer. Even seemingly harmful chemicals like food colorings have been shown to affect attention span and contribute to attention deficit hyperactivity disorder in children. (McCarthy, 2021)

Perfumes, deodorants, toothpastes, hair products, cleaning products, industrial chemicals, and on and on and on... What has a century of high-chemical use, particularly those applied directly to or ingested by the body—the kind that simply didn't exist in the thousands of years of human evolution before their creation, done to us? Do we even fully know yet? As science writer and co-founder of the Council for the Human Future, Julian Cribb, explains, our chemical emissions are six times greater than our greenhouse gas emissions. (Cribb, 2021) Hundreds of billions of tonnes of chemical emissions will affect the future of our species—and every other species, in untold ways. Some estimates place the annual global fatality range caused by the use and disposal of chemicals at around nine-million. (Cribb, 2021) Plastics are some of the greatest chemical threats. A conference on plastic pollution held by the United Nations suggested that the plastic particles in our ocean are now five-hundred times greater than the number of stars in our galaxy! (UNEP, 2017) Alarming studies have predicted that in the absence of drastic changes in the ways we deal with and dispose of chemicals, the world's oceans could be devoid of fish by 2048. (Worm, 2006) Dead seas would essentially mean the end of human life on Earth. The University of South Australia's Professor Ravi Naidu puts it bluntly: "Most humans are now, to some degree, contaminated by industrial chemicals." He goes on, "Wherever we look, from the deep oceans and remotest islands to the peaks of the highest mountains, to the snows of Antarctica, to the stratosphere, we find traces of man-made chemicals, many of them linked to or suspected of causing cancers and other diseases." (CRC, 2013) We are not on a sustainable evolutionary path.

Our evolvability going forward will rely on the conditions we've created for ourselves. Nature may no longer present a serious threat in the form of predators (just try to avoid any lions you run into), but the climate crisis we've created is already presenting new natural threats in the form of drought, rising seas, fire, etcetera. And the unnatural environments we've created, like dense urban living, technology use, and cultural practices, are already starting to shape our evolution as well. When we transitioned to a diet that included dairy and grains, our genes evolved to allow us to digest milk and starch. (Perry, 2007) When we started leaving the countryside in favor of city living, our DNA mutated to build up new resistance to certain bacteria. (Galvani, 2003) As we began to live more sedentary, social lives, starting around 10,000-20,000 years ago, our brains began to evolve to be smaller. (DaSilva, 2021; Stibel, 2021) Not to worry though. Size isn't everything. Orcas and elephants have larger brains than us, but they're not as sophisticated. And as it turns out, Einstein's brain was smaller than average, too, and look what it was capable of! (Longrich, 2022)

Some scientists argue that for humans especially, the process of natural selection as proposed by Darwin no longer applies in the same way as it used to—that humans essentially stepped off the evolutionary ladder. (Templeton, 2010; Sample, 2007) But others say that's not the whole picture. Despite natural selection playing a lesser role in how we've evolved in recent millennia, research shows that we've actually adapted a great deal in the last 50,000 years. In fact, as many as two-thousand genes, or 7% of the human genome, have gone through extensive evolution during this timeframe. From an adaptive perspective, our genetic evolution is actually accelerating. (Hawkes, 2007)

Geneticist Chris Wills sees this adaptive form of evolution as key to mapping humanity's evolutionary future. He thinks it will be all about the brain (even if they are becoming a little smaller). "The essence of human beings is their intelligence and at the present time people have an enormous range of different abilities. My prediction is one of the ways we'll evolve is to add genes that increase our range of abilities." (Sample, 2007) *Add genes.* Hmmm… Sounds like biohacking, doesn't it?

And where else will major changes occur? Scientists envision five key areas where our genes will adapt in the next few thousand years: fertility, intelligence, immunity, appearance, and nutrition. (Sample 2007) The process of 'gene editing' has all kinds of moral and ethical dilemmas baked into it, but it's not hard to imagine that we're headed toward so-called *designer babies,* where eye and hair colour, and any number of other physical or cognitive characteristics could be added-to-cart at your doctor's office.

And as new technologies emerge, particularly in electromagnetic and subtle energy forms, our ability to target specific cells, genes, and even traits, will likely expand. Imagine entraining genes to thrive on our modern high-carbohydrate diets rather than succumbing to them? We could use frequency to eradicate obesity. Imagine using frequency to manipulate the cells in certain areas of our brains. We could encourage new and stronger neural pathways, capable of expanding our analytical or creative faculties. The possibilities could be endless!

A QUANTUM TOMORROW

Quantum physics has shown us, as I've broken down for you in previous chapters, that every cell in our body is in constant motion and vibration, creating resonance. This resonance is a roadmap. It's a blueprint to understanding imbalance, dysregulation, and desynchronization. We can use our body's resonant frequencies to better understand how energy modifies and maintains our health and wellness, to restore our bodies' homeostatic state—to balance our Qi.

As Dr. Eric Leskowitz's work points out, many plausible and testable energy-based models for treatment are already taking form. He proposes a medical field where 'energy physiology' and 'subtle anatomy' serve as a guide for how energy can serve as a primary component of health and illness. (Leskowitz, 2022) I agree wholeheartedly. By recognizing the role of our resonant frequencies, we can better align cause and effect, ushering in a new era of diagnostic advances.

Pioneering bioelectromagnetic researcher Glen Rein goes even further. He sees the biofield as central to the future of healing, serving as a "resonance target for external forms of energy". He writes, "The functional role of the biofield in the body's innate self-healing mechanisms is hypothesized, based on the concept of bioinformation which, mediated by consciousness, functions globally at the quantum level to supply coherence, phase, spin, and pattern information to regulate and heal all physiologic processes." (Rein, 2004)

Quantum electrodynamics is almost certainly where our new frontier of science is taking us. It's just over the horizon. "There is support from recent advances in quantum biology, which demonstrate that coherence, as a state of order of matter coupled with electromagnetic fields, is one of the key quantum phenomena supporting life dynamics." As electrical engineer Antonio Manzalini, and surgeon specialist in internal medicine Bruno Galeazzi explain, all of the parts of our bodies, from cells, to tissues, to organs, "are characterized by their own specific wave functions, whose phases are perfectly orchestrated in a multi-level coherence oneness. When this multi-level coherence is broken, a disease emerges." (Manzalini, 2019)

And it's not just electromagnetic energy as defined by physics as we know it that forms this brighter tomorrow. The spiritual-consciousness side of biofield and aura research is on the rise, too. Theoretical foundations for how these energy fields operate are becoming clearer the more scientists are willing to be brave and set aside their own biases, and negative stigma from their peers. Electromagnetic fields, biophotons, quantum processes, coherent phase states, and even the quantum vacuum itself, which we explored earlier, are becoming exciting and illuminating areas of focus. Many scientists believe "the existence of the biofield challenges reductionist approaches," and that its relation to our biology will serve to "inform an integrated understanding of consciousness and the living universe". (Kafatos, 2015)

As you've seen throughout this book, tapping into that *living universe* and its subtle energy means that healing energy doesn't have to be generated by a physical device. It can be generated, cultivated, and transmitted by the individual as well, by accessing higher conscious and interdimensional states of being—by synchronizing ourselves to travel the energy strands of the cosmic web. Researchers like Dr. Paul Rosch have recognized this in many academic publications, bucking the mainstream trend and offering evidence-based models for the reality of subtle energy's healing powers. "It is fully accepted that good health depends on good communication both within the organism and between the organism and its environment. Sophisticated imaging procedures brought to bear on telomere, stem cell, and genetic research are confirming the ability of meditation and some other traditional practices to promote optimal health." (Rosch, 2009)

Think back to the superhumans we met in Chapter 5. For many of them, their meditative abilities allow them to control some of their bodies' biochemical processes at will. Meditation is not just a means of maintaining centered mental health. It can enable truly awesome optimizing powers over our bodies and minds. It can transcend the boundaries of physics. Incorporating the wisdom of energy masters and healers into our approach to health and wellness will open new doors of possibility.

Many EM advocates are working hard on fast-tracking that incorporation. One organization's work has certified more than sixteen-hundred energy healing practitioners through intense two-year training programs. These practitioners have worked with hundreds-of-thousands of people all around the world to address physical and cognitive imbalances with responsive energy approaches. I agree with these groups that the anomalies that mainstream subtle energy and fifth force research see as challenges today, both in terms of explanation and in application, present massive opportunities for the future of "energy-informed" healthcare, which seeks to "address biological activities at their energetic foundations", to regulate "physiological processes with speed and precision", and to promote "healing and prevention of illness with interventions that can be economically and noninvasively applied." (Eden, 2020)

The dominant, mainstream biomedical paradigm sees healthcare mostly through the lenses of surgery and chemicals. It sees 'life as chemistry'. (Rubik, 2015) It fails to recognize more fundamental, elemental, cosmic principles. It fails to see our bodies, minds, and spirits as parts of the greater cosmic tapestry that weaves and binds us to the universe. I believe, as do so many others—and our numbers are growing, that we must transition away from this model, from this blind, reactionary ignorance.

We *must* start seeing 'life as *energy*'. We must embrace a life of Qi. This is the surest way of supercharging the future of humanity, firmly establishing the science of life force as the bedrock of an integrative approach to wellness.

I don't just believe... I *know*... that in just a few years' time, we will be living in a new age of health and wellness. An era of energy-powered homeostasis. We will be detecting diseases long before they become problematic. We will drastically reduce the need for drugs and surgeries, eradicating the need for them altogether in some cases. We will use a full spectrum of energy forces to re-atomize our physical dysregulation. We'll extend our lifespan, but more importantly our health-span. We'll transcend the perceived limits of human cognition and consciousness, finally tapping into the parts of our brain that we never access, and learning how to navigate those new neural pathways to manifest unimaginable realities. We will shape a healthcare and medicine landscape where exponential advancement upends what being sick or unwell looks like. And we will say goodbye to some of the most devastating illnesses that we face today, particularly the degenerative mental illnesses that deprive so many of well-deserved dignity during their golden years.

I hope in these pages that I've opened your mind by even the tiniest fraction, and that through that crack in the so-called *settled science*, you've been energized by wavelengths of new possibility. This book, like my life, and the work I've found to engage in, is the product of the subtle energy we've examined and explored together here.

As I was falling from that third-floor balcony all those years ago as a child, I never could have imagined that it would lead me to where I am today. With every passing day, I find myself more driven and eager to share the transformative awakening of a life powered by the flow of Qi. My own experiences, and those of the many thousands I've met who have used my technology and others like it, instruct and inform a clearer vision for a healing revolution. The fog that once obscured my purpose lifted long ago, and where I once chased after that lantern in the mist, I now try my best to serve as a lantern and beacon for others.

If this book has served as that lantern for you, I encourage you to share it, and its message, with others, but more than that, I *challenge you* to take on your own personal Qi journey. You now have a wealth of information and resource options to completely reimagine your life and to carry out a transformative shift in personal well-being. The ways in which you've been addressing your physical and cognitive conditions may be working to various extents, but don't you owe it to yourself to find out if an energy-based approach can manage your symptoms, or complement your existing therapy, in a radically more efficient, targeted, and effective way? I don't just want you to use specific devices though; I want you to shift your perspective on how a life well-lived should look. I challenge you to seek out higher states of consciousness, to deepen your sense of existence. By harmonizing your Qi, I know you will open yourself up to abundance and enable your Qi-powered manifesting abilities. I know you can become superhuman.

My lifelong passion has become this harmonizing process of continual self-transformation in order to achieve the full potential of a resonant Qi life. Part of that process is helping other truth seekers, just like *you,* to transform themselves quickly and easily.

So I ask you this: will *you take on this challenge?* Will you indulge your own conscious awakening? Will you join me in shaping the future of energy medicine? Will you help open the minds of others—your friends, family, and colleagues, so they too can experience a transformative life? Together, we can synchronize our collective resonance. We can speed up the scientific revolution. We can reach the next great frontier of human ingenuity, and evolve not just biologically, but individually and societally. We can live a Qi-filled life. We can change our frequency. We can change our reality.

Your life of Qi awaits. Your journey begins.

If you believe, as I do, that the future is a healing one, reliant on the amazing powers that universal Qi has to offer, I invite you to reach out today. Arrange a personal consultation with our Qi Life experts to review your health and wellness and address the key areas where energy healing can benefit your overall well-being. Together we can unlock your body's innate healing and manifestation powers.

>>> Visit QiLife.health to book your consultation today.

And if you're ready to take the ultimate leap in energy healing and join me at the vanguard of the scientific revolution we've explored in this book, my Inner Circle is ready to welcome you with open arms. Your next level of personal awakening, transformation, and evolution begins now...

- **Unlock your body's innate healing** and manifestation powers
- **Change your thought patterns** to create a life you love
- **Discover who you truly are** and release your hidden potential
- **Transmute your suffering**, amplify your field, and attract abundance fast
- **Boost your Qi energy** and learn and increase your income quickly
- **Access private opportunities** and closely held secrets for joy and wealth

Your path to freedom and abundance awaits. Learn exclusive techniques, take part in private energy healing sessions, discover unique Inner Circle Frequencies, and more more...

Inner Circle membership isn't available to everyone. Access requires that you be in good standing in the community, that you will support your fellow elite group members, that you will only use the technology for good, and that you wish to improve yourself and others. Attract abundance, manifest your desires, and raise your resonant frequency with my personalized, direct guidance and attention.

>>> Visit www.DavidWongInnerCircle.com to apply for Inner Circle membership!

LEARN MORE
START YOUR QI LIFE JOURNEY

Get Your Free Meditation Frequency
www.UseTheQi.com

Download Our Apps
www.QiCoilApp.com

Discover Automated Energy Healing
www.QiEnergy.Ai

Shop Qi Coils™
www.GetQiCoils.com

Take the 30-Day Qigong Meditation Challenge
www.LearnSuperhuman.com

Experience the World's Most Powerful Meditation Frequencies
www.HigherQuantum.com

Professional Frequency Therapy Systems For Practitioners
www.QiLifeTherapy.com

Your Next Level of Transformation
www.DavidWongInnerCircle.com

Book a Consultation with a Technology Expert
www.QiLife.health

Change your frequency.
Change your reality.
Change your life.

REFERENCES

Allais, M. (1959). *New Theoretical and Experimental Research Work on Gravity.* (Report). Memoir prepared to compete for 'Gravity Research Foundation' prize.

Allais, M. (1959). Should the Laws of Gravitation Be reconsidered? Part I – Abnormalities in the Motion of a Paraconical Pendulum on an Anisotropic Support. *Aero/Space Engineering,* 18, 46–52.

Allais, M. (1959). Should the Laws of Gravitation Be reconsidered? Part II – Experiments in Connection with the Abnormalities Noted in the Motion of the Paraconical Pendulum with an Anisotropic Support. *Aero/ Space Engineering,* 46, 51-56.

Allais, M. (1999). *The 'Allais Effect' and my experiments with the paraconical pendulum* (1954-1960) [Report]. Memoir C-6083 prepared for NASA.

Alrais, A., Alfadeel, E., & Hamouda, S. (2017). Schumann Resonances and Their Potential Applications: A Review Article. *Mordovia University Bulletin,* 27, 476-489.

Ander, M., et al. (1989). Test of Newton's Inverse-Square Law in the Greenland Ice Cap. *Physical Review Letters,* 62(9), 985–988.

Anderson, J., Hagerdorn, P., Gunstad, J., & Spitznagel, M. (2018). Using Coffee to Compensate for Poor Sleep: Impact on Vigilance and Implications for Workplace Performance. *Applied Ergonomics,* 70, 142–147.

Anderson, M. (2009, March 25). New Cold Fusion Evidence Reignites Hot Debate. *IEEE Spectrum.* www.spectrum.ieee.org/new-cold-fusion-evidence-reignites-hot-debate

Arata, Y., & Zhang, Y. (2008, March). Establishment of the "Solid Fusion" Reactor. (Report) New Energy Times. Translated by *New Energy Times* from original Japanese. www.newenergytimes.com/v2/library/2008/2008Arata-EstablishmentOfTheSolidFusionReactor-March.pdf

Arden, G., & Sivaprasad, S. (2012). The Pathogenesis of Early Retinal Changes of Diabetic Retinopathy. *Documenta Ophthalmologica*, 124(1), 15–26.

Arp, H. (2000). What Has Science Come To?. *Journal of Scientific Exploration*, 14(3), 447-454.

Avildsen, J. (Director). (1984). *Karate Kid* [Film]. Delphi II Productions.

Ayling, K., & the Editors of Fate Magazine (1968) *Strange World of the Occult*. Paperback Library, Inc.

Baconnier, S., Lang, S., Polomska M., Hilczer, B., Berkovic, G., & Meshulam, G. (2002). Calcite Microcrystals in the Pineal Gland of the Human Brain: First Physical and Chemical Studies. *Bioelectromagnetics*, 23(7), 488-495.

Bae, J.M., Jung, H.M., Hong, B.Y., Lee, J.H., Choi, W.J., Lee, J.H., & Kim, G.M. (2017). Phototherapy for Vitiligo. *JAMA Dermatology*, 153(7), 666–674.

Balbir, N., & Siddhāntacakravartin, N. (2010). *Dravyasamgraha*. Pandit Nathuram Premi Research Series.

Baldwin, A.L., & Schwartz, G.E. (2006). Personal Interaction with a Reiki Practitioner Decreases Noise-Induced Microvascular Damage in an Animal Model. *Journal of Alternative and Complementary Medicine*, 12(1), 15–22.

Baldwin, A.L., Wagers, C., & Schwartz, G.E. (2008). Reiki Improves Heart Rate Homeostasis in Laboratory Rats. *Journal of Alternative and Complementary Medicine*, 14(4), 417-422.

Baldwin, A.L., Et al. (2013). Comparison of Physical Therapy with Energy Healing for Improving Range of Motion in Subjects with Restricted Shoulder Mobility. *Evidence-Based Complementary and Alternative Medicine*, eCAM, 2013.

Baldwin A.L., & Trent N.L. (2017). An Integrative Review of Scientific Evidence for Reconnective Healing. *Journal of Alternative & Complementary Medicine*, 23(8), 590-598.

Banerjea, A.K. (2014). Philosophy of Gorakhnath with Goraksha-Vacana-Sangraha. *Motilal Banarsidass*, 13, 297-299.

Barbault, A., Costa, F.P., Bottger, B., Munden, R.F., Bomholt, F., Kuster, N., & Pasche, B. (2009). Amplitude-Modulated Electromagnetic Fields for the Treatment of Cancer: Discovery of Tumor-Specific Frequencies and Assessment of a Novel Therapeutic Approach. *Journal of Experimental & Clinical Cancer Research*, 28(1), 51.

Barling, S. (2003, February 13). Cosmic Degrees: Out of Body at the Monroe Institute. *The Hook*, 0206, and also published online at: www. readthehook.com/93054/cover-story-cosmic-degrees-out-body-monroe-institute

Bartel, L., Clements-Cortes, A., Ahonen, H., Evans, M., & Freedman, M. (2016). Short-Term Effects of Rhythmic Sensory Stimulation in Alzheimer's Disease: An Exploratory Pilot Study. Journal of Alzheimer's Disease, 52, 651–660.

Bartel, L., Braun, J.T., Paneduro, D., Picard L., & Gordon, A. (2019a). A Parallel Randomized Controlled Trial Examining the Effects of Rhythmic Sensory Stimulation on Fibromyalgia Symptoms. *PLoS One*, 14(3).

Bartel, L., Braun, J.T., Al Shirawi, M.I., Rotzinger, S., & Kennedy, S.H. (2019b). A Pilot Study Investigating the Effect of Music-Based Intervention on Depression and Anhedonia. *Front. Psycho.*, 10.

Bartlett, R. (2007). *Matrix Energetics – The Science and Art of Transformation*. Beyond Words Publishing.

BBC News, by Whitehouse, D. (2000, March 10). *New Light on Dark Matter*. www.news.bbc.co.uk/2/hi/science/nature/670207.stm

Beckley A.M., & Wright E.S. (2021). Identification of Antibiotic Pairs That Evade Concurrent Resistance Via a Retrospective Analysis of Antimicrobial Susceptibility Test Results. *The Lancet. Microbe*, 2(10), 545–554.

Belenky, I., Tagger, C., & Bingham, A. (2015). Intense Pulsed Light Pulse Configuration Manipulation Can Resolve the Classic Conflict Between Safety and Efficacy. *Journal of Drugs in Dermatology*, 14(11).

Bentov, I. (1977). *Stalking the Wild Pendulum: On the Mechanics of Consciousness*, E.P. Dutton.

Benveniste, J. (1993a). Transfer of Biological Activity by Electromagnetic Fields. *Frontier Perspectives*, 3(2), 113-115.

Benveniste, J. (1993b). Molecular Signaling at High Dilution or by Means of Electronic Circuitry. *Journal of Immunology*, 150.

Benveniste, J. (1994a). Transfer of the Molecular Signal by Electronic Amplification. *FASEB Journal*, 8.

Benveniste, J. (1994b). Further Biological Effects Induced by Ultra High Dilutions. Inhibition by a Magnetic Field. In: Endler, P.C., & Schulte, J. (eds) *Ultra High Dilution*. Springer.

Benveniste, J., (1995a). Electronic Transmission of the Cholinergic Signal. *FASEB Journal*, 9.

Benveniste, J. (1995b). Direct Transmission to Cells of a Molecular Signal Via an Electronic Device. *FASEB Journal*, 9.

Benveniste, J. (1999, March 10). *Electromagnetically Activated Water and the Puzzle of the Biological Signal* [Presentation]. Cavendish Departmental Colloquium, Cambridge, England. www.sms.cam.ac.uk/media/871684

Berger, H. (1929). Über das Elektroenkephalogramm des Menschen. *Arch. Psychiatr.*, 87, 527–570.

Berginer, V.M., & Cohen, H.R. (2006). The Nature of Goliath's Visual Disorder and the Actual Role of his Personal Bodyguard, *Ancient Near Eastern Studies*, 43, 27-44.

Berryman, S. (2008). Ancient Atomism. *The Stanford Encyclopedia of Philosophy* [Fall 2008 Edition]. E. Zalta (Ed.)

Bertone, G., Hooper, D., & Silk, J. (2005). Particle Dark Matter: Evidence, Candidates and Constraints. *Physics Reports*, 405(5–6), 279–390.

Betts, J. Gordon, K.A., Young, J.A. Wise, Johnson E., Poe, B., Kruse, D.H., Korol, O., Johnson, J.E., Womble, M., & DeSaix, P. (2013). *Anatomy and physiology*. OpenStax.

Billington, R.A., Bruzzone, S., De Flora, A., Genazzani, A.A., Koch-Nolte, F., Ziegler, M., & Zocchi, E. (2006). Emerging Functions of Extracellular Pyridine Nucleotides. *Mol. Med.*, 12(11–12), 324–327.

Bjorvatn, B., & Pallesen, S. (2009). A Practical Approach to Circadian Rhythm Sleep Disorders. *Sleep Medicine Reviews*, 13(1), 47–60.

Blessing, W.W. (1997). Inadequate Frameworks for Understanding

Bodily Homeostasis. *Trends in Neurosciences*, 20(6), 235–239.

Blom, J. (2009). *A Dictionary of Hallucinations*. Springer.

Blomkamp, N. (Director). (2013). *Elysium* [Film]. TriStar Pictures.

Bogan, K.L., & Brenner, C. (2008). Nicotinic Acid, Nicotinamide, and Nicotinamide Riboside: A Molecular Evaluation of NAD+ Precursor Vitamins in Human Nutrition. *Annual Review of Nutrition*, 28, 115–130.

Bouzari, N., Elsaie, M.L., & Nouri, K. (2012). Laser and Light for Wound Healing Stimulation. In Nouri, K. (ed.). *Lasers in Dermatology and Medicine*. Springer, 267–75.

Braibant, S., Giacomelli, G., & Spurio, M. (2011). *Particles and Fundamental Interactions: An Introduction to Particle Physics* (Illustrated ed.). Springer Science & Business Media, 109.

Braibant, S., Giacomelli, G., & Spurio, M. (2012). *Particles and Fundamental Interactions: An introduction to particle physics* (2nd Ed.). Springer.

Braidy, N., Villalva, M.D., & Eeden, S.V. (2020). Sobriety and Satiety: Is NAD+ the Answer?. *Antioxidants*, 9(5), 425.

Brian, D. (2001). *The Voice of Genius: Conversations with Nobel Scientists and Other Luminaries*. Basic Books.

Bronfort, G., Nilsson, N., Haas, M., Evans, R., Goldsmith, C.H., Assendelft, W.J., & Bouter, L.M. (2004). Non-Invasive Physical Treatments for Chronic/Recurrent Headache. *The Cochrane Database of Systematic Reviews*, 3.

Brosseau, L., Welch, V., Wells, G.A., de Bie, R., Gam, A., Harman, K., Morin, M., Shea, B., & Tugwell, P. (2005). Low Level Laser Therapy (Classes I, II and III) for Treating Rheumatoid Arthritis. *Cochrane Database of Systematic Reviews*, 2010(4).

Bruyere, R.L. (1994). *Wheels of Light-Chakras, Auras, and the Healing Energy of the Body*, A Fireside Book. Simon and Schuster.

Bürkle, A. (2005). Poly(ADP-ribose). The Most Elaborate Metabolite of NAD+. *FEBS J.*, 272 (18), 4576–89.

Burr, H.S. (1972). *Blueprint for Immortality – The Electric Patterns of Life*. The C.W. Daniel Company, Ltd.

Buser, P.A., & Imbert, M. (1992). Vision. MIT Press.

Cade, C.M., & Coxhead, N. (1979). *The Awakened Mind: Biofeedback and the Development of Higher States of Awareness*. Wildwood House Limited.

Cantor, D.S., & Evans, J.R. (2013). *Clinical Neurotherapy: Application of Techniques for Treatment*. Academic Press.

Carr, T. (2017, August 3). Too Many Meds? America's Love Affair with Prescription Medication. *Consumer Reports*. www.consumerreports. org/prescription-drugs/too-many-meds-americas-love-affair-with-prescription-medication/#nation

Carrington, H. (1975) *Laboratory Investigations into Psychic Phenomena*. Ayer Company Publishers, Inc.

Carroll, R.T. (Date unknown). Telepathy. In *The Skeptic's Dictionary*. Retrieved April, 2022, from: www.skepdic.com/telepath.html

Cartlidge, E. (2016). Has a Hungarian Physics Lab Found a Fifth Force of Nature?. *Nature*.

Cayce, E.E., & Cayce, H.L. (1971). *The Outer Limits of Edgar Cayce's Power*. Association for Research and Enlightenment.

Chaieb, L., Wilpert, E.C., Reber, T.P., & Fell, J. (2015). Auditory Beat Stimulation and Its Effects on Cognition and Mood States. *Front Psychiatry*, 12(6).

Chalovich, J.M. (2012). Franklinization: Early Therapeutic Use of Static Electricity. *ScholarShip*, East Carolina University.

Chaumery, L., & de Belizal, A. (2013). *Essai de Radiesthesie Vibratoire*. DERVY.

Chen, J. (2007). *Philosopher, Practitioner, Politician: The Many Lives of Fazang*. Brill.

Chen, K., & Yeung, R. (2002). Exploratory Studies of Qigong Therapy for Cancer in China. *Integrative Cancer Therapies*, 1(4), 345-370.

Cherry, N.J. (2002). Schumann Resonances, a Plausible Biophysical Mechanism for the Human Health Effects of Solar/Geomagnetic Activity. *Natural Hazards*, 26(3), 279-331.

Cherry, N.J. (2003). Human Intelligence: The Brain, An Electromagnetic

System Synchronized by the Schumann Resonance Signal. *Medical Hypotheses*, 60(60), 843-844.

Chiao, R.Y., Ropers, C., Solli, D., & Hickmann, J.M. (2002). *Faster-Than-Light Propagations and their Applications. Coherence and Quantum Optics VIII*. Springer.

Childs, B.G., Durik, M., Baker, D.J., & van Deursen, J.M. (2015). Cellular Senescence in Aging and Age-Related Disease: from Mechanisms to Therapy. *Nature Medicine*, 21(12), 1424–1435.

Chomsky, N. (2000). *New Horizons in the Study of Language and Mind*. Cambridge University Press.

Chow, R., Johnson, M., Lopes-Martins, R., & Bjordal, J. (2009). Efficacy of Low-Level Laser Therapy in the Management of Neck Pain: a Systematic Review and Meta-Analysis of Randomised Placebo or Active-Treatment Controlled Trials. *Lancet*, 374(9705), 1897–1908.

Chown, M. (2011, August 17). Really Dark Matter: Is the Universe Made of Holes?. *New Scientist*. Retrieved March, 2022, from: www.newscientist.com/article/mg21128262-200-really-dark-matter-is-the-universe-made-of-holes/

Cicoli, M., Pedro, F.G., & Tasinato, G. (2012). Natural Quintessence in String Theory. *Journal of Cosmology and Astroparticle Physics*, 2012(7).

CIE (International Commission on Illumination). (1987). *International Lighting Vocabulary*. Archived 27 February 2010 at the Wayback Machine. Number 17.4. CIE, (4th ed.).

Clare, I.S. (1897). *Library of Universal History, Volume 2: Ancient Oriental Nations and Greece*. R. S. Peale, J. A. Hill.

Clark, A.A., Devoret, M.H., Girvin, S.M., Marquardt, F., & Schoelkopf, R.J. (2010). Introduction to Quantum Noise, Measurement, and Amplification. *Reviews of Modern Physics*, 82(2).

Clark, A.V. (1973). *Psychokinesis-Moving Matter with the Mind*. Parker Publishing Company.

ClearHarmony.net. (2005, July 28). *Ancient Cultivation Stories: Zhuge Liang's Cultivation Practices*. Retrieved April, 2022, from: www.clearharmony.net/articles/a27920-Ancient-Cultivation-Stories-Zhuge-Liang's-Cultivation-Practise.html#.Ymx4IC8r1B0

Cobb, C.M. (2006). Lasers in Periodontics: A Review of the Literature. *Journal of Periodontology*, 77(4), 545–564.

Cockburn, H. (2019, November 21). Scientists May Have Discovered Fifth Force of Nature, Laboratory Announces. *Independent.*

Cohen, K.S. (1999). The Way of Qigong: The Art and Science of Chinese Energy Healing. Random House of Canada.

Congressional Record. (2012). *Volume 158*, 18504-18505. U.S. Government Publishing Office.

Copi, C.J., Schramm, D.N., & Turner, M.S. (1995). Big-Bang Nucleosynthesis and the Baryon Density of the Universe. *Science*, 267(5195), 192–199.

Cory, C. (Director). (2020). Superhuman: *The Invisible Made Visible* [Film]. Omnium Media, 1091 Pictures.

Cramer, J.G. (1995, December). Tunneling Through the Lightspeed Barrier. *Analog Science Fiction and Fact Magazine.*

Crawford, S.E., Leaver, V.W., & Mahoney, S.D. (2006). Using Reiki to Decrease Memory and Behavior Problems in Mild Cognitive Impairment and Mild Alzheimer's Disease. *The Journal of Alternative and Complementary Medicine*, 12(9), 911-913.

Cribb, J. (2021). Earth Detox. In *Earth Detox: How and Why We Must Clean Up Our Planet*. Cambridge University Press.

CRC for Contamination Assessment and Remediation of Environment. (2013). Eminent Scientist Warns of Global Contamination Risks. *Phys.org*. Retrieved March, 2022, from: www.phys.org/news/2013-02-eminent-scientist-global-contamination.html

Cubb, T. (2008). The Arata Demonstration: A Review Summary. *Infinite Energy*, 80, 12-15.

Da Silva, J. P., Traniello, J.F.A., Claxton, A.G., & Fannin, L.D. (2021). When and Why Did Human Brains Decrease in Size? A New Change-Point Analysis and Insights from Brain Evolution in Ants. *Frontiers in Ecology and Evolution*, 9.

Da Silva, J. P., Da Silva, M.A., Almeida, A.P.F., Junior, I.L., & Matos, A.P. (2010). Laser Therapy in the Tissue Repair Process: A Literature Review. *Photomedicine and Laser Surgery*, 28(1), 17–21.

Davidson, D. (1997). *Shape Power: A Treatise on How Form Converts Universal Aether into Electromagnetic and Gravitic Forces and Related Discoveries in Gravitational Physics*. Rivas Publishing.

Davies, P.C.W., & Gribbin, J. (1992). *The Matter Myth: Dramatic Discoveries that Challenge our Understanding of Physical Reality*. Simon & Schuster.

de Belizal, A., & Morel, P.A. (1965). *Physique Micro-Vibratoire et Forces Invisibles*, Desforges.

Dean, D. (1966). Plethysmograph Recordings as ESP Responses. *International Journal of Neuropsychiatry*, 2, 439-446.

Department of the Navy. (1990). Command History of USS Dolphin (AGSS 555) for CY89. (Report)

Devenish, R.P. (2013). *The Hermitage Meditation Manual: All You Need to Know to Properly Learn to MeditateI*. Dharma Fellowship Publications.

Devereux, P. (1999). *Places of Power-Measuring the Secret Energy of Ancient Skies*. Blandford.

Devereux, P. (2003). *Fairy Paths & Spirit Roads*. Chrysalis.

Diep, C., Ftouni, S., Manousakis, J.E., Nicholas, C.L., Drummond, S.P.A., & Anderson, C. (2019). Acoustic Slow Wave Sleep Enhancement Via a Novel, Automated Device Improves Executive Function in Middle-Aged Men. *Sleep*, 43(1).

Diepersloot, J. (2000). *The Tao of Yiquan: The Method of Awareness in the Martial Arts*. Center For Healing & The Arts.

Diffey, B.L. (1980). Ultraviolet Radiation Physics and the Skin. *Phys. Med. Biol*, 25(3), 405–426.

Dispenza, J. (2019). *Becoming Supernatural: How Common People are Doing the Uncommon*. Hay House, inc.

Dodson, E.R., & Zee, P.C. (2010). Therapeutics for Circadian Rhythm Sleep Disorders. *Sleep Medicine Clinics*, 5(4), 701–715.

Donald, R.G., & Anderson, A.S. (2011). Current Strategies for Antibacterial Vaccine Development. In Miller, P.F. (ed.). *Emerging Trends in Antibacterial Discovery: Answering the Call to Arms.* Horizon Scientific Press

Dong, P. (1984). *The Four Major Mysteries of Mainland China.* Prentice-Hall.

Dong, P., & Raffill, T.E. (1997). *China's Super Psychics.* Marlow and Company.

Dong, P., & Raffill, T.E. (2006). *Empty Force: The Power of Chi for Self-Defense and Energy Healing,* North Atlantic Books.

Dougherty, T.J. (1998). Photodynamic Therapy. *JNCI: Journal of the National Cancer Institute.* 90(12), 889–905.

Dougherty, T. (2020, June). USS Dolphin (AGSS-555) – The "Triple Nickel – The Last U.S. Diesel Submarine. *The Submarine Historian,* p. 33-51. Retrieved April, 2022, from: www.navsource.org/archives/08/pdf/0855505.pdf

Duchenne (de Boulogne), G.B. (1876). *Mécanisme de la physionomie humaine.* (2nd ed.). Ve Jules Renouard.

Dunn, H.H. (1931). Movie New Eye of Microscope in War on Germs. *Popular Science,* 118(6).

Dvorsky, G. (2016, March 27). This Biohacker Used Eyedrops to Give Himself Temporary Night Vision. *Gizmodo.* Retrieved April, 2022, from: www.io9.gizmodo.com/this-biohacker-used-eyedrops-to-give-himself-temporary-1694016390

Dzang, K. (1993). Bioelectromagnetic Fields as a Material Carrier of Biomagnetic Information. *Aura-Z,* 3, 42-54.

Economic Times. (2012, November 2). Matter Undermined. Retrieved March, 2022, from: www.economictimes.indiatimes.com/opinion/vedanta/matter-undermined/articleshow/17055344.cms

Eden, D., & Feinstein, D. (2020). Development of a Healthcare Approach Focusing on Subtle Energies: The Case of Eden Energy Medicine. *Advanced Mind Body Medicine,* Summer, 34(3), 25-36.

Edwards, P., ed. (1972). *The Encyclopedia of Philosophy,* 1-4.

Einstein, A. (1920). *Ether and the Theory of Relativity.* Methuen.

Einstein, A., & Lawson, R.W. (1921). *Relativity: The Special and General Theory*. Holt.

Ellinger, F. (1957). *Medical Radiation Biology*. Charles C. Thomas.

Emerson, D.W. (2014). The Lodestone, from Plato to Kircher. *Preview*, 2014(173), 52-62.

EPRI (Electric Power Research Institute). (1994). *Development of Energy Production Systems from Heat Produced in Deuterated Metals: Volume 1*, TR-107843.

Everett, H. (1957). Relative State Formulation of Quantum Mechanics. *Reviews of Modern Physics*, 29(3), 454–462.

Everett, H., Wheeler, J.A., DeWitt, B.S., Cooper, L.N., Van Vechten, D., & Graham, N. (1973) *The Many-Worlds Interpretation of Quantum Mechanics*, Princeton Series in Physics. Princeton University Press.

Eysenck, H.J. (1957). *Sense and Nonsense in Psychology*. Penguin.

Fell, J., & Axmacher, N. (2011). The Role of Phase Synchronization in Memory Processes. *Nature Reviews Neuroscience*, 12(2), 105–118.

Fischbach, E., Sudarsky, D., Szafer, A., Talmadge, C., & Aronson, S.H. (1986). Reanalysis of the Eötvös Experiment. *Physical Review Letters*, 56(1), 3–6.

Fleischmann, M., & Pons, S. (1989). Electrochemically Induced Nuclear Fusion of Deuterium. *Journal of Electroanalytical Chemistry*, 261(2), Part 1, 301-308.

Fludd, R. (1659). *Mosaical Philosophy*. Humphrey Moseley.

Foster, J.J., Sutterer, D.W., Serences, J.T., Vogel, E.K., & Awh, E. (2017). Alpha-Band Oscillations Enable Spatially and Temporally Resolved Tracking of Covert Spatial Attention. *Psychological Science*, 28(7), 929–941.

Franciscus, & Krabice z Veitmile, B. (1784). *Francisci Chronicon Pragense: Item Benessii de Weitmil Chronicon ecclesiae Pragensis*. Volume 2 of *Scriptores rerum Bohemicarum*. (F.M. Pelcl, Ed.).

Frantzis, B.K. (2008). *The Chi Revolution: Harnessing the Healing Power of Your Life Force*. Blue Snake Books.

Frati, P., Kyriakou, C., Del Rio, A., Marinelli, E., Vergallo, G.M., Zaami,

S., & Busardò, F.P. (2015). Smart Drugs and Synthetic Androgens for Cognitive and Physical Enhancement: Revolving Doors of Cosmetic Neurology. *Current Neuropharmacology*, 13(1), 5–11.

Frawley, D., & Ranade, S. (2001). *Ayurveda, Nature's Medicine*. Lotus Press.

Frawley, D. (2009). *Inner Tantric Yoga: Working with the Universal Shakti: Secrets of Mantras, Deities and Meditation*. Lotus Press.

Friedman, A. (1922). *Über die Krümmung des Raumes. Zeitschrift für Physik*. 10 (1), 377–386. Translated in Friedmann, A. (1999). *On the Curvature of Space. General Relativity and Gravitation*, 31(12), 1991–2000.

Fries, P. (2005). A Mechanism for Cognitive Dynamics: Neuronal Communication Through Neuronal Coherence. *Trends in Cognitive Sciences*, 9(10), 474–480.

Fulleylov-Krause, B.K., Sison, S.L., & Ebert, A.D. (2020). Nicotinamide Mononucleotide Treatment Increases NAD+ Levels in an iPSC Model of Parkinson's Disease. *bioRxiv* (online pre-print), Retrieved March, 2022, from: www.biorxiv.org/content/10.1101/2020.05.06.080911v1

Galvani, A.P., Slatkin, M. (2003). Evaluating Plague and Smallpox as Historical Selective Pressures for the *CCR5-Δ32* HIV-Resistance Allele. *PNAS*, 100(25).

Gardiner, D.J. (1989). Practical Raman *spectroscopy*. Springer-Verlag.

Gariaev, P.P., Grigoriev, K.V., Vasiliev, A.A., Poponin, V.P., and Shcheglov, V.A. (1992). Investigation of the Fluctuation Dynamics of DNA Solutions by Laser Correlation Spectroscopy. *Bulletin of the Lebedev Physics Institute*, 11(12), 23-30.

Gerber, R. (2001). *Vibrational Medicine*. Bear & Company.

Gersi, D. (1991). *Faces in the Smoke-An Eyewitness Experience of Voodoo, Shamanism, Psychic Healing and Other Amazing Powers*. Jeremy P. Tarcher.

Geynits, A.V., Moskvin, S.V., Achilov, A.A. (2012). *Внутривенное лазерное облучение крови [Intravenous Laser Blood Irradiation]* (in Russian). M.–Tver: Triada.

Ghosh, P. (2021, March 23). Machine finds tantalizing hints of new physics. *BBC News*. Retrieved April, 2022, from: www.bbc.com/news/science-environment-56491033

Ghosh, P. (2021, April 7). Muons: 'Strong' evidence found for a new force of nature. *BBC News.* Retrieved March, 2022, from: www.bbc.com/news/56643677

Gibbs, P. (1997). *Is Faster-Than-Light Travel or Communication Possible?* [Presentation] Usenet Physics FAQ at University of California, Riverside, CA.

Goldsby, T., Goldsby, M., McWalters, M., & Mills, P. (2016). Effects of Singing Bowl Sound Meditation on Mood, Tension, and Well-being. *Journal of Evidence-Based Complementary & Alternative Medicine,* 22.

Gomes, A.P., Et. al. (2013). "Declining NAD+ Induces a Pseudohypoxic State Disrupting Nuclear-Mitochondrial Communication during Aging. *Cell,* 155(7), 1624–1638.

Goodwin, TJ. (2003). Physiological and Molecular Genetic Effects of Time-Varying Electromagnetic Fields on Human Neuronal Cells. *NASA Technical Publication* [United States Government].

Graves, D. (2018). Lessons From Tesla for Plasma Medicine. *IEEE Transactions on Radiation and Plasma Medical Sciences.*

Green, E.E., Parks, P.A., Guyer, P.M., Fahrion, S.L., & Coyne, L. (1993). Anomalous Electrostatic Phenomena in Exceptional Subjects. *Subtle Energies,* 2, 69.

Gribbin, J. (2012). Erwin Schrödinger and the *Quantum Revolution.* Wiley.

Gris, H., & Dick, W. (1978). *The New Soviet Psychic Discoveries.* Prentice-Hall.

Gu, H. (1978). *The Nature Journal* (Chinese), Vol. 1.

Gu, M. (2009). *An Introduction to Wisdom Healing Qigong.* Petaluma.

Gu, M. (2011). *Wisdom Healing (Zhineng) Qigong: Cultivating Wisdom and Energy for Health, Healing and Happiness.* Petaluma.

Guiley, R. (1991). *Harper's Encyclopedia of Mystical and Paranormal Experience.* Harper.

Hainsworth, L.B. (1983). The Effect of Geophysical Phenomena on Human Health. *Speculations in Science and Technology,* 6(5), 439-444.

Hainsworth, L.B. (1987). Electrical Technology and Human Evolution. *Speculations in Science and Technology,* 11(2), 101.

Hamblin, M.R. (2017). Ultraviolet Irradiation of Blood: "The Cure That Time Forgot"?. *Advances in Experimental Medicine and Biology*, 996, 295–309.

Hanegraaff, W.J. (2006). *Dictionary of Gnosis & Western Esotericism*. Brill.

Harrison, S.J., Et. al. (2015). Light Therapy and Serotonin Transporter Binding in the Anterior Cingulate and Prefrontal Cortex. *Acta Psychiatrica Scandinavica*, 132(5), 379–388.

Hausdorf, H. (1994). The Chinese Roswell, New Paradigm Books. Originally published in German by Langen, A., & Muller Verlag, G., as *Die Weisse Pyramide*. F.A. Herbig Verlagsbuchhandlung GmbH.

Hawks, J., Wang, E.T., Cochran, G.M., Harpending, H.C., & Moyzis, R.K. (2007). Recent Acceleration of Human Adaptive Evolution. *PNAS*, 104(52).

Hayles, K. (1999). How We Became Posthuman: Virtual Bodies in Cybernetics, Literature, and Informatics. University of Chicago Press.

Hecht, L. (2010). In Appreciation of Maurice Allais (1911-2010) The New Physical Field of Maurice Allais. *21st Century Science & Technology*, 26–30.

Heindel, J.J., Blumberg, B., Cave, M., Et al. (2017). Metabolism Disrupting Chemicals and Metabolic Disorders. *Reproductive Toxicology*, 68, 3–33.

Heisenberg, W. (1962). *Physics and Philosophy: The Revolution in Modern Science*. Harper & Row Publishers, Inc.

Herbermann, C, Ed. (1913). 'Matter'. *Catholic Encyclopedia*. Robert Appleton Company.

Hill, D., Et. al. (Director). (2010-2014). *Stan Lee's Superhumans* [Documentary TV series]. Off the Fence, A&E Home Video.

Hin, O.K. (2010). *Zhineng Qigong: The Science, Theory and Practice*. CreateSpace.

Holland, A. (2000). *Voices of Qi: An Introductory Guide to Traditional Chinese Medicine*. North Atlantic Books.

Huang, J. (1987). *The Primordial Breath, Vol. 1*. Original Books, Inc.

Huang, Z., Et. al. (2015). The Effectiveness of Low-Level Laser Therapy for Nonspecific Chronic Low Back Pain: A Systematic Review and Meta-Analysis. *Arthritis Research & Therapy*, 17, 360.

Hughes, J. (2011). *Transhumanism.* In W. Bainbridge, Ed., *Leadership in Science and Technology: A Reference Handbook.* Sage Publications.

Hurley, M.V., & Bearne, L.M. (2008). Non-Exercise Physical Therapies for Musculoskeletal Conditions. *Best Practice & Research: Clinical Rheumatology,* 22(3), 419–33.

Hyman, R. (1985). *A Critical Historical Overview of Parapsychology.* In P. Kurtz, Ed., A Skeptic's Handbook of Parapsychology. Prometheus Books.

Iannone, A.P. (2001). *Dictionary of World Philosophy.* Taylor & Francis.

IEEE (Institute of Electrical and Electronics Engineers). (1997). The *IEEE Standard Dictionary of Electrical and Electronics Terms* (6th ed).

Jahn, R.G., Dunne, B.J., & Nelson, R.D. (1987). Engineering Anomalies Research. *Journal of Scientific Exploration,* 1(1), 21-50.

Jahn, R. (1992, December 15). [Press release] *Society for Scientific Exploration.* www.jse.com/PR_Princeton_92.html

Janakiramaiah, N., Et al. (2000). Antidepressant Efficacy of Sudarshan Kriya Yoga (SKY) in Melancholia: A Randomized Comparison with Electroconvulsive Therapy (ECT) and Imipramine. *Journal of Affective Disorders,* 57(1-3), 255-259.

Japsen, B. (2009, June 15). AMA Report Questions Science Behind Using Hormones as Anti-Aging Treatment. *The Chicago Tribune.* Retrieved March, 2022, from: www.articles.chicagotribune.com/2009-06-15/news/0906140132_1_anti-aging-hormones-ama-council

Jerabeck, J., & Pawluk, W. (1998). *Magnetic therapy in eastern Europe: A Review of 30 Years of Research.* W. Pawluk.

Jonas, W.B., & Crawford, C.C. (2003). Science and Spiritual Healing: A Critical Review of Spiritual Healing, "Energy" Medicine, and Intentionality. *Alternative Therapies in Health and Medicine,* 9(2), 56-61.

Jones, J.P. (2006, May 12-14). *An Extensive Laboratory Study of Pranic Healing Using Medical Imaging and Laboratory Methods* [Conference presentation). World Pranic Healers' Convention, Mumbai, India.

Jones, J.P. (2008). *The Dose of Gamma Radiation Given to Cells Was Set at "2 Grays," Which Established the 50% Survival Rate After 24 Hours* [Personal communication with C. Swanson, Dr.], in Swanson. C. (2010). Life Force: The Scientific Basis. Poseidia Press.

Jones, N. (1938, May 6). Dread Disease Germs Destroyed by Rays, Claim of S.D. Scientist: Cancer Blow Seen After 18-year Toil by Rife. *San Diego Evening Tribune.*

Kafatos, M.C., Et. al. (2015). Biofield Science: Current Physics Perspectives. *Glob Adv Health Med*, 4, 25-34.

Kapstein, M.T. (2014). Buddhist Idealists and Their Jain Critics on Our Knowledge of External Objects. *Royal Institute of Philosophy Supplement*, 74, 123–147.

Karim, I. (2016). *BioGeometry Signatures: Harmonizing the Body's Subtle Energy Exchange with the Environment.* CreateSpace Independent Publishing Platform.

Kilner, W.J. (1911). *The Human Atmosphere or The Aura Made Visible by the Aid of Chemical Screens.* Rebman.

Kim, E.J., & Um, S.J. (2008). SIRT1: Roles in Aging and Cancer. BMB Rep., 41(11), 751–756.

Kliempt, P., Ruta, D., Ogston, S., Landeck, A., & Martay, K. (1999). Hemispheric-Synchronisation During Anaesthesia: A Double-Blind Randomised Trial Using Audiotapes for Intra-Operative Nociception Control. *Anaesthesia*, 54(8), 769–773.

Knott, E.K. (1948). Development of Ultraviolet Blood Irradiation. *American Journal of Surgery*, 76(2), 165–171.

Kolodny, L. (1968). When Apples Fall. *Moscow Pravda.* Partial translation in *Journal of Paraphysics*, 2(4).

Korotkov, K. (2002). Human Energy Field: Study with GDV *Bioelectrography.* Backbone Publishing.

Korotkov, K. (2006). *Spiral Traverse: Journey into the Unknown.* Kirlionics Technologies International.

Kozyrev, N.A. (1958). *Causal or Nonsymmetric Mechanics in a Linear Approximation.* Pulkovo.

Kozyrev, N.A. (1976). The Origin of Stellar Energy on the Basis of the Analysis of Observational Data. Journal of Astrophysics, 12(2).

Krivit, S.B. (2008). Arata-Zhang LENR Demonstration. *New Energy*

Times. Retrieved March, 2022, from: www.newenergytimes.com/v2/news/2008/29img/Arata-Demo.shtml

Krivit, S.B. (2008) Low Energy Nuclear Reactions: The Emergence of Condensed Matter Nuclear Science. *American Chemical Society.* Retrieved March, 2022, from: www.pubs.acs.org/doi/pdf/10.1021/bk-2008-0998.ch001

Kroeling, P., Et. al. (2013). Electrotherapy for neck pain. *The Cochrane Database of Systematic Reviews*, 8.

Kroupa, P. (2010). Local-Group Tests of Dark-Matter Concordance Cosmology: Towards a New Paradigm for Structure Formation. *Astronomy and Astrophysics*, 523.

Kuiken, T. (2016). Governance: Learn from DIY Biologists. *Nature Magazine*, 531(7593), 167–168.

Kulin, Y.T (1980). *Bioelectretic Effect.* Washington Research Center. Translated from Russian, published by *Science and Tehnics.*

Kurz, O., & Rejdak, Z. (1968). *About Telekinesis.* Pravda.

LA Times (1940, June 26). *Giant Microscope May Yield Secrets of Bacteria World.*

Labbé, P., Et. al. (2007). Forty Years of Erratic Insecticide Resistance Evolution in the Mosquito Culex Pipiens. *PLoS Genetics*, 3(11).

LaMothe, J.D. (1972, July) *Controlled Offensive Behaviour-USSR.* Defense Intelligence Agency Task No. T72-01-14 (Report No. ST-CS-01-172.

Lang, S., Et. al. (1996). Piezoelectricity in the Human Pineal Gland. *Bioelectrochemistry and Bioenergetics - BIOELECTROCHEM BIOENERG*, 41, 191-195.

Laszlo, E. (2004). *Science and the Akashic Field: An Integral Theory of Everything.* Inner Traditions.

Lau, D.C. (2003). *Mencius* (Revised ed.). Chinese University Press.

Lautrup, S. (2019). NAD+ in Brain Aging and Neurodegenerative Disorders. *Cell Metabolism*, 30(4), 630-655.

Lawrence, R., & Rosch, P. (1998). *Magnet Therapy Book: The Pain Cure Alternative.* Prima Publication.

Lazzerini Ospri, L., Prusky, G., & Hattar, S. (2017). Mood, the Circadian System, and Melanopsin Retinal Ganglion Cells. *Annual Review of Neuroscience*, 40(1), 539–556.

Lee, E., Koo, J., & Berger, T. (2014). UVB Phototherapy and Skin Cancer Risk: A Review of the Literature. *Int. J. Dermatol*, 44(5), 355–360.

Le Scouarnec, R.P., Poirier, R.M., Owens, J.E., Gauthier, J., Taylor, A.G., & Foresman, P.A. (2001). Use of Binaural Beat Tapes for Treatment of Anxiety: A Pilot Study of Tape Preference and Outcomes. *Alternative Therapies in Health and Medicine*.

Leskowitz. E. (2022). A cartography of Energy Medicine: From Subtle Anatomy to Energy Physiology. *Explore*, 2, 152-164.

Lewis, A.K., Osborn, I.P., & Roth, R. (2004). The Effect of Hemispheric Synchronization on Intraoperative Analgesia. *Anesthesia and Analgesia*, 98(2), 533–536.

Li, J., Et. al. (2017). A Conserved NAD Binding Pocket that Regulates Protein-Protein Interactions During Aging. *Science*, 355(6331), 1312–1317.

Liang, S.Y., Wu, W.C., Breiter-Wu, D. (1997). *Qigong Empowerment: A Guide to Medical, Taoist, Buddhist, and Wushu Energy Cultivation*. Way of the Dragon Pub.

Licht, S (1967). *History of Electrotherapy: Therapeutic Electricity and Ultraviolet Radiation*. Waverly.

Liddell, H.G., &; Scott, R. (1940). *A Greek-English Lexicon* (Sir H.S. Jones, & R. McKenzie, Eds.) Clarendon Press.

Liu, H., M.D., & Perry, P. (1997). *Mastering Miracles*. Warner Books.

Liu, H. (2006). *The Chinese Overseas*. Taylor & Francis.

Lloyd, G.E.R. (1968). *Aristotle: The Growth and Structure of his Thought*. Cambridge University Press.

Lochtefeld, J.G. (2002). *The Illustrated Encyclopedia of Hinduism*: A-M. Rosen Publishing Group.

Loizzo, J.J. (2016). The Subtle Body: An Interoceptive Map of Central Nervous System Function and Meditative Mind-Brain-Body Integration. *Annals of the New York Academy of Sciences*. Wiley, 1373(1), 78–95.

Lomas T., Ivtzan I., & Fu, C.H. (2015). A Systematic Review of the Neurophysiology of Mindfulness on EEG Oscillations. *Neuroscience & Biobehavioral Reviews*, 57,401–410.

Long, M.F. (1948). *The Secret Science Behind Miracles*, DeVORSS & Co.

Longrich, N. (2022, March 1). Future Evolution: From Looks to Brains and Personality, How Will Humans Change in the Next 10,000 Years?. *The Conversation*. Retrieved March, 2022, from: www.theconversation. com/future-evolution-from-looks-to-brains-and-personality-how-will-humans-change-in-the-next-10-000-years-176997

López-Otín, C., Blasco, M.A., Partridge, L., Serrano, M., & Kroemer, G. (2013). The Hallmarks of Aging. *Cell*, 153(6): 1194–1217.

Lu, K.Y. (1969). *The Secrets of Chinese Meditation: Self-Cultivation by Mind Control as Taught in the Ch'an, Mahāyāna and Taoist Schools in China*. S. Weiser.

Lu, Z. (1997). *Scientific Qigong Exploration – The Wonders and Mysteries of Qi*. Amber Leaf Press.

Lynes, B. (1987). *The Cancer Cure That Worked!: Fifty Years of Suppression*. BioMed Publishing Group.

Lynes, B. (2017). *Rife's Great Discovery: Why "Resonant Frequency" Therapy Is Kept Hidden from Public Awareness*. BioMed Publishing Group.

Ma, J.R. 馬濟人. (1992). 實用中醫氣功學 (*Practical Qigong for Traditional Chinese Medicine*). Shanghai Scientific and Technical Publishers 上海科学技术出版社.

Ma Y., & Chua, S.L. (2021). No Collateral Antibiotic Sensitivity by Alternating Antibiotic Pairs. *The Lancet Microbe*, 3(7).

Mair, V.H. (1994). *The Biography of Hua-t'o from the "History of the Three Kingdoms"*, In V.H. Mair (ed.). *The Columbia Anthology of Traditional Chinese Literature*. Columbia University Press.

Malenka, R.C., Nestler, E.J., Hyman, S.E., & Holtzman, D.M. (2015). *Higher Cognitive Function and Behavioral Control. Molecular Neuropharmacology: A Foundation for Clinical Neuroscience* (3 ed.). McGraw-Hill Medical.

Mallinson, J., & Singleton, M. (2017). *Roots of Yoga*. Penguin Books.

Malone, A., Et. al. (Executive Producer). (1980). *Cosmos: A Personal*

Journey [TV series]. PBS – KCET Los Angeles.

Mandelbaum, W.A. (2000). *The Psychic Battlefield: A History of the Military-Occult Complex.* Thomas Dunne Books.

Manzalini, A., & Galeazzi, B. (2019). *Explaining Homeopathy with Quantum Electrodynamics.* Homeopathy.

Martin, E. (2008). *A Dictionary of Biology* (6th ed.). Oxford University Press.

Masunaga, S. (2017, April 21). A Quick Guide to Elon Musk's New Brain-Implant Company, Neuralink. *Los Angeles Times.* Retrieved March, 2022, from: hwww.latimes.com/business/technology/la-fi-tn-elon-musk-neuralink-20170421-htmlstory.html

McCarthy, C (2021). Common Food Additives and Chemicals Harmful to Children. *Harvard Health Blog.* Retrieved March, 2022, from: www.health.harvard.edu/blog/common-food-additives-and-chemicals-harmful-to-children-2018072414326

McCraty, R., Atkinson, M., Stolc, V., Alabdulgader, A. A., Vainoras, A., & Ragulskis, M. (2017). Synchronization of Human Autonomic Nervous System Rhythms with Geomagnetic Activity in Human Subjects. *International Journal of Environmental Research and Public Health, 14*(7), 770.

McMoneagle, J. (1999, November 14). [Conference presentation]. Project Awareness Conference, Clearwater, FL, United States.

McTaggart, L. (2001). *The Field.* HarperCollins.

Mendoza, R. (1995). *The Acentric Labyrinth.* Harper Collins.

Merlo, L.M., Pepper, J.W., Reid, B.J., & Maley, C.C. (2006). Cancer as an Evolutionary and Ecological Process. *Nature Reviews. Cancer, 6*(12), 924–935.

Miller, R.A., & Miller, I. (2003). *Schumann's Resonances and Human Psychobiology,* O.A.K.

Mishlove, J. (2000). The PK Man: *A True Story of Mind Over Matter.* Hampton Roads Publishing.

Mitchell, E. (1971). An ESP Test from Apollo 14. *Journal of Parapsychology,* 35, 89-107.

Mitchell, J.L., Ph.D. (1987). *Out of Body Experiences-A Handbook.* Ballantine Books.

Michell, J. (1969). *The View Over Atlantis.* Sago.

Mohan, A.G. (2010). *Krishnamacharya: His Life and Teachings.* Shambhala.

Moller, K.I., Et. al. (2014). How Finsen's Light Cured Lupus Vulgaris. *Photodermatol Photoimmunol Photomed.*, 21(3), 118–124.

Monroe, R. (1985). *Journeys Out of the Body.* Anchor/Doubleday.

Monroe, R. (1985). *Far Journeys.* Doubleday.

Monroe, R. (1994). *Ultimate Journey.* Doubleday.

Montiel, I., Bardasano, J.L., & Ramos, J.L. (2005). *Biophysical Device for The Treatment of Neurodegenerative Diseases.* In A. Méndez-Vilas (ed.). (2003, October 13-18). *Recent Advances in Multidisciplinary Applied Physics.* [Conference presentation]. First International Meeting on Applied Physics (APHYS-2003), Badajoz, Spain.

Morgane, P.J., Galler, J.R., & Mokler, D.J. (2005). A Review of Systems and Networks of the Limbic Forebrain/Limbic Midbrain. *Progress in Neurobiology*, 75(2), 143–160.

Morton, C.A., Et. al. (2002). Guidelines for Topical Photodynamic Therapy: Report of a Workshop of the British Photodermatology Group. *British Journal of Dermatology, 146(4), 552–567.*

Moskowitz, C. (2015, September 9). Two Accelerators Find Particles That May Break Known Laws of Physics. *Scientific American.* Retrieved March, 2022, from: www.scientificamerican.com/article/2-accelerators-find-particles-that-may-break-known-laws-of-physics1/

Motoyoshi, A. (2000). Teleportation Without Resorting to Bell Measurement. *Physics Letters A*, 270, 293-295.

Muller, F.M. (2003). *Six Systems of Indian Philosophy; Samkhya and Yoga; Naya and Vaiseshika.* Kessinger Publishing.

Murphy, D.T. (1935). *Mortality Statistics: 1932* [Report]. U.S Department of Commerce: Bureau of the Census, United States Government Printing Office.

Murray, A.T. (1919). *Homer, The Odyssey with an English Translation. Perseus Digital Library Project.* Harvard University Press.

NASA (National Aeronautics and Space Administration). (2013, May 28). *Schumann Resonance*. J. Wilson, Ed. Retrieved May, 2022, from: www.nasa.gov/mission_pages/sunearth/news/gallery/schumann-resonance.html

Naumann, N. (2000). *Japanese Prehistory: The Material and Spiritual Culture of the Jōmon Period*. Otto Harrassowitz Verlag.

Navas, L.E., & Carnero, A. (2021). NAD+ Metabolism, Stemness, the Immune Response, and Cancer. *Sig. Transduct Target Ther.*, 6(2).

Neely, J.N. (2009). Distance Healing Experiment with Pennsylvania State University Medical School. *Natural Healing Center*. Retrieved April, 2022, from: www.naturalhealingcenter.com/creative/jixingli.htm (2009)

Newman, T.B., Et. al. (2009). Numbers Needed to Treat with Phototherapy According to American Academy of Pediatrics Guidelines. *Pediatrics*, 123(5).

Niedermeyer, E., & da Silva, F.L. (2004). *Electroencephalography: Basic Principles, Clinical Applications, and Related Fields*. Lippincott Williams & Wilkins.

Nielsen, M. (2007). *Introduction to Yang-Mills Theories* [personal working notes]. Retrieved March, 2022, from: www.michaelnielsen.org/blog/yang_mills.pdf

Neumayer, P., & Stark, R. (2013). *Painting the Energy Body: Signs and Symbols for Vibrational Healing*. Healing Arts Press.

New York Times. (November 22, 1931). *Bacilli Revealed by New Microscope; Dr. Rife's Apparatus, Magnifying 17,000 Times, Shows Germs Never Before Seen*.

Neve, P. (2007). Challenges for Herbicide Resistance Evolution and Management: 50 Years After Harper. *Weed Research*, 47(5), 365–369.

Nojonen, M. (2009). *Jymäyttämisen taito. Strategiaoppeja muinaisesta Kiinasta* (translated: The Art of Deception. Strategy lessons from Ancient China). Gaudeamus.

Novack, G. (1979). *The Origins of Materialism*. Pathfinder Press.

Oberoi, S., Et, al. (2014). Effect of Prophylactic Low Level Laser Therapy on Oral Mucositis: A Systematic Review and Meta-Analysis. *PLoS One*, 9(9).

Oerter, R. (2006). *The Theory of Almost Everything: The Standard Model, the Unsung Triumph of Modern Physics* (Kindle ed.). Penguin Group.

Oginska, H., & Oginska-Bruchal, K. (2014). Chronotype and Personality Factors of Predisposition to Seasonal Affective Disorder. *Chronobiology International*, 31(4), 523–531.

Osler, M. (2010). *Reconfiguring the World.* The Johns Hopkins University Press.

Osnaghi, S., Et. al. (2009). The Origin of the Everettian Heresy. *Studies in History and Philosophy of Modern Physics*, 40(2), 97–123.

Ossola, A. (2015, November 18). These Biohackers Are Creating Open-Source Insulin. *Popular Science.* Retrieved March, 2022, from: www.popsci.com/these-biohackers-are-making-open-source-insulin/

Oster, G. (1973). Auditory Beats in the Brain. *Scientific American*, 229(4), 94–102.

Ostrander, S., & Schroeder, L. (1970). *Psychic Discoveries Behind the Iron Curtain.* Bandtam Books.

Padmanabhan, R., Hildreth, A.J., & Laws, D. (2005). A Prospective, Randomised, Controlled Study Examining Binaural Beat Audio and Pre-Operative Anxiety in Patients Undergoing General Anaesthesia for Day Case Surgery. *Anaesthesia.*

Pagés Ruiz, F. (2001). Krishnamacharya's Legacy. *Yoga Journal*, May/June Ed.

Pan, D., Xue, W., Zhang, W., Liu, H., & Yao, X. (2012). Understanding the Drug Resistance Mechanism of Hepatitis C Virus NS3/4A to ITMN-191 Due to R155K, A156V, D168A/E Mutations: A Computational Study. *Biochimica et Biophysica Acta (BBA) - General Subjects*, 1820(10), 1526–1534.

Pantaleone, J. (2002). Synchronization of Metronomes. *American Journal of Physics*, 70(10), 992–1000.

Paulson, G.L. (1998). *Kundalini and the Chakras: A Practical Manual--Evolution in This Lifetime* (1st ed.). Llewellyn Publications.

Patrizi, A., Raone, B., & Ravaioli, G.M. (2015). Management of Atopic Dermatitis: Safety and Efficacy of Phototherapy. *Clinical, Cosmetic and Investigational Dermatology*, 8, 511–520.

Pawluk, W. (2015). Magnetic Fields for Pain Control (M. Markov, Ed.). Chapter 17 in: *Electromagnetic Fields in Biology and Medicine.* CRC Press.

Pavlova, L P. (1967, August 4). Results and Discussions of Experiments with the Nedra-20 [Conference presentation]. Also: *Some Electroencephalographic Indices in Experimental Research in Bio-telecommunication.* Seminar of Technical Parapsychology Section affiliated All-Union Engineering Institute, Moscow, U.S.S.R.

Pearce, J.M. (2012). Building Research Equipment with Free, Open-Source Hardware. *Science,* 337(6100), 1303–1304.

Pei, S., Inamadar, A.C., Adya, K.A., & Tsoukas, M.M. (2015). Light-Based Therapies in Acne Treatment. *Indian Dermatol Online J.,* 6(3), 145–57.

Perkins, D. (1999). *Encyclopedia of China: The Essential Reference to China, Its History and Culture.* Checkmark Books.

Perry, G., Et. al. (2007). Diet and the Evolution of Human Amylase Gene Copy Number Variation. *Nat Genet.,* 39, 1256–1260.

Poponin, V. (2002). The DNA Phantom Effect: Direct Measurement of a New Field in the Vacuum Substructure. *WebCom.* Retrieved March, 2022, from: www.webcom.com./hrtmath.IHM/Research/DNAPhantom. htm, also in http://homepags.ihug.co.nz/~sai/DNAPhantom.htm

Potter, K.H., & Arya, U. (1977). *Indian Metaphysics and Epistemology.* Motilal Banarsidass Publications.

Poulain, M., Et. al. (2004). Identification of a Geographic Area Characterized by Extreme Longevity in the Sardinia Island: The AKEA Study. *Experimental Gerontology,* 39(9), 1423–1429.

Powell, A. (2019). Longevity and Anti-Aging Research: 'Prime Time for an Impact on the Globe. *The Harvard Gazette, Health & Medicine.* Retrieved March, 2022, from: www.news.harvard.edu/gazette/story/2019/03/anti-aging-research-prime-time-for-an-impact-on-the-globe/

Powell. A.E. (1925). *The Etheric Double-The Health Aura,* Quest Books, Theosophical Publishing House.

Powell, A.E. (1927). *The Astral Body,* Quest Books, The Theosophical Publishing House.

Powell, A.E. (1928). *The Causal Body and the Ego,* Stellar Books, a Division of the Philippine Theosophical Society.

Powell, A.E. (1982). *The Mental Body,* Theosophical Publishing House, Ltd.

Price, P. (1983). *Bells & Man.* Oxford University Press.

Puthoff, H.E. (1974). Information Transmission Under Conditions of Sensory Shielding. *Nature*, 251(18), 602-607.

Puthoff, H.E., Targ, R., & May, E.C. (1981). *Experimental Psi Research: Implications for Physics*, in R.G. Jahn (ed.), *The Role of Consciousness in the Physical World.* Westview Press, Inc.

Radin, D. (1997). *The Conscious Universe.* Harper Collins.

Radin, D., Ph.D., Machado, F.R., & Zangari, W. (2001). Effects of Distant Healing Intention Through Time & Space: Two Exploratory Studies. *Subtle Energies & Energy Medicine*, 11(3), 207.

Rao, P. (2017). *The Yogi Who Walked to His Destiny.* Onlinegatha.

Ratra, P., & Peebles, L. (1988). Cosmological Consequences of a Rolling Homogeneous Scalar Field. *Physical Review D.*, 37(12), 3406–3427.

Ravaioli, F.T., Et. al. (2010). *Fundamentals of Applied Electromagnetics* (6th ed.). Prentice Hall.

Rebhan, E. (2017). Model of a Multiverse Providing the Dark Energy of Our Universe. *International Journal of Modern Physics* A, 32(25).

Rein G. (2004). Bioinformation Within the Biofield: Beyond Bioelectro-magnetics. *J. Altern. Complement Med.*, 10(1), 59-68.

Rejdak, Z. (1969). The Kulagina Cine Film. *Journal of Paraphysics*, 3(3).

Reports and Data. (2020, February 19). Nootropics Market to Reach USD 5.32 Billion By 2026 | Reports and Data. *GlobeNewswire News Room.* Retrieved March, 2022, from: www.globenewswire.com/news-release/2020/02/19/1987135/0/en/Nootropics-Market-To-Reach-USD-5-32-Billion-By-2026-Reports-And-Data.html

Rheingold, H. (2000). Tools for Thought. *Howard Rheingold.* Retrieved March, 2022 from: www.rheingold.com/texts.tft/5.html

Rinpoche, M. (2009). *Luminous Essence: A Guide to the Guhyagarbha Tantra.* Snow Lion.

Ritter, M. (1997, December 10). Beam Me Up—Science Fact: Scientists Achieve 'Star Trek'-like Feat. *Associated Press.*

Rizzi, M., & Schindelin, H. (2002). Structural Biology of Enzymes Involved in NAD and Molybdenum Cofactor Biosynthesis. *Curr. Opin. Struct. Biol.*, 12(6), 709–720.

Robbins, P.D., Et. al. (2021). Senolytic Drugs: Reducing Senescent Cell Viability to Extend Health Span. *Annual Review of Pharmacology and Toxicology*, 61(1), 779–803.

Robinson, N.G. (2013). Complementary and Alternative Veterinary Medicine: Laser Therapy. *The Merck Veterinary Manual*, (11th ed.).

Rogers, J.M. (1990). Arts of War in Times of Peace. Swordsmanship in Honchō Bugei Shōden (Chapter 5). *Monumenta Nipponica*, 45(4), 413-447.

Rogo. D.S. (1983). *Leaving the Body-A Complete Guide to Astral Projection.* Prentice Hall Press.

Rosch, P.J. (2009). Bioelectromagnetic and Subtle Energy Medicine: The Interface Between Mind and Matter. *Ann. N.Y. Acad. Sci.*, 1172, 297-311.

Rosenthal, R., & Rubin, D.B. (1978). Impersonal Expectancy Effects: The First 345 Studies. *Behavioural and Brain Sciences*, 3, 377-415.

Ross, C.L. (2019). Energy Medicine: Current Status and Future Perspectives. *Global Advances in Health and Medicine*, 8.

Rothwell, J.F., & Storms, E. (2008). *Report on Arata's Paper and Lecture about his "Solid Fusion" Reactor* (Report). LENR-CANR.

Rubik, B., Muehsam, D., Hammerschlag, R., & Jain, S. (2015). Biofield Science and Healing: History, Terminology, and Concepts. *Glob. Adv. Health Med*, 4, 8-14.

Sacks, D. (1997). *A Dictionary of the Ancient Greek World*. Oxford University Press US.

Sadoulet, B. (2007). Particle Dark Matter in the Universe: At the Brink of Discovery?. *Science*, 315(5808), 61-63.

Saladin, K. (2011). *Human Anatomy* (3rd ed.). McGraw-Hill.

Sample, I. (2007, December, 15). Where Do We Go From Here?. *The Guardian*. Retrieved March, 2022, from: www.theguardian.com/science/2007/dec/15/genetics.evolution

Samuel, G. (2013). *Religion and the Subtle Body in Asia and the West: Between Mind and Body*. Routledge.

Sanders, A.J., Et. al. (2000). Project SEE (Satellite Energy Exchange): An International Effort to Develop a Space-Based Mission for Precise Measurements of Gravitation. *Classical and Quantum Gravity*, 17(12).

Saraswati, S.S. (1981). Prana: The Universal Life Force. *Yoga Magazine.*

Savrov, L.A., & Yushkin, V.D. (1995). Paraconical Pendulum as a Detector of Gravitational Effects During Solar Eclipses (Processing Data and Results). *Measurement Techniques, Springer Science+Business Media*, 38(1), 9–13.

Savrov, L.A. (1995). Paraconical Pendulum as a Detector of Gravitational Effects During Solar Eclipses (Processing Data and Results). *Measurement Techniques, Springer Science+Business Media*, 38(3), 253–260.

Savrov, L.A. (1997). Experiment with Paraconic Pendulums During the November 3, 1994 Solar Eclipse in Brazil. *Measurement Techniques, Springer Science+Business Media*, 40(6), 511–516.

Savrov, L.A. (2009). Improved Determination of Variation of Rate of Rotation of Oscillation Plane of a Paraconic Pendulum During the Solar Eclipse in Mexico on July 11, 1991. *Measurement Techniques, Springer Science+Business Media*, 52(4), 339–343.

Saxl, E.J., & Allen, M. (1971). 1970 Solar Eclipse as 'Seen' by a Torsion Pendulum. *Physical Review D*, 3(4), 823–825.

Schleicher, C. (1988). [Monograph]. Mankind Research Unlimited, Inc.

Schnabel, J. (1997). *Remote Viewers: The Secret History of America's Psychic Spies.* Dell.

Schnitzler, A., & Gross, J. (2005). Normal and Pathological Oscillatory Communication in the Brain. *Nature Reviews Neuroscience*, 6(4), 285–296.

Schombert, J. (2015). *Professorial Glossary* (Version 7.0). University of Oregon. Retrieved March, 2022, from: www.abyss.uoregon.edu/~js/glossary/equivalence_principle.html

Schröedinger, E. (1984). *General Scientific and Popular Papers.* In Collected Papers, 4. Austrian Academy of Sciences. Braunschweig/Wiesbaden: Vieweg & Sohn.

Schumann, W.O. (1952). Ueber die strahlungslosen Eigenschwingungen einer leitenden Kugel, die von einer Luftschicht und einer Ionosphaerenhuelle umgeben ist, *Z.Naturforsch*, 7(a),149.

Schumann W.O., & König, H. (1954). Ueber die Beobachtung von Atmospherics bei geringsten Frequenzen. *Naturwissenschaften*, 41, 183.

Schutlz, M.B., & Sinclair, D.A. (2016). Why NAD+ Declines During Aging: It's Destroyed. *Cell Metabolism*, 23(6), 965-966.

Schwarzschild, B. (1988). From Mine Shafts to Cliffs – The 'Fifth Force' Remains Elusive. *Physics Today*, 41.

Sedacca, M. (2017, January 30). The Multiverse Is an Ancient Idea. *Nautilus*. Retrieved April, 2022, from: www.nautil.us/the-multiverse-is-an-ancient-idea-10262/

Sergeyev, G.A. (1967, December 3) *On the Nature of the Experimental Research of Dr. Zdenek Rejdak* [Seminar presentation]. Seminar of Technical Parapsychology Section Affiliated, All Union Engineering Institute, Moscow, U.S.S.R.

Sergeyev, G., Pavlova, L., & Romankenko, A. (1968). *Statistical Method of Research of the Human EEG*. Academy of Science, USSR. Science Publishing.

Sergeyev, G.A., & Kulagin, V.V. (1972a). The Interaction of Bioplasmic Fields of Living Organisms with Light Photon Sources, in *Bioenergetics Questions (Material of the Scientific Methodological Seminar in Alma-Ata)*, Edited by B.A. Dombrovsky, G.A. Sergeyev, & B.M. Inyushin. Southern California Society for Psychical Research.

Sergeyev, G.A., & Kulagin, V.V. (1972b). Characteristics of Bioplasmic Energy, in *Bioenergetics Questions (Material of the Scientific Methodological Seminar in Alma-Ata)*, Edited by B.A. Dombrovsky, G.A. Sergeyev, & B.M. Inyushin. Southern California Society for Psychical Research.

Shade, C. (2020). The Science Behind NMN-A Stable, Reliable NAD+Activator and Anti-Aging Molecule. *Integrative Medicine*, 19(1), 12-14.

Shakhparanov, I.M. (1998). Kosyrev-Dirac Emanation: Methods of Detecting and Interaction with Matter. *Journal of New Energy*, 2(3-4).

Shakhparanov, I.M. (2001). Interaction of Matter and Methods of Detecting. *New Energy Technologies*, 1, 275-280.

Sharma, A. (2006). *A Primal Perspective on the Philosophy of Religion*. Springer Verlag.

Sharratt, A. (2019, October 16). The Healing Power of sound: Studies Show Sound Baths Can Improve Not Only Mood but Also Physical Symptoms Such as Chronic Pain. *The Globe and Mail.*

Sheldrake, R. (1999). *Dogs That Know When Their Masters Are Coming Home.* Three Rivers Press.

Shepherd, A.J. (1954). *Rudolph Steiner: Scientist of the Invisible.* Inner Traditions International.

Shipov, G.I. (2004). Dark Energy in the Theory of the Physical Vacuum. *Uvitor Shipov.* Retrieved March, 2022, from: www.shipov.com

Shore, A.G. (2004). Long Term Effects of Energetic Healing on Symptoms of Psychological Depression and Self-Perceived Stress. *Alternative Therapies in Health and Medicine, 10(3), 42-48.*

Siegfried, T. (1999, July 5). Hidden Space Dimensions May Permit Parallel Universes, Explain Cosmic Mysteries. *The Dallas Morning News.*

Sinclair, D. (2019). *Lifespan: Why We Age – and Why We Don't Have To.* Simon & Schuster.

Singer, D.W. (1941). The Cosmology of Giordano Bruno (1548-1600). *Isis,* 33(2), 187-196.

Sivin, N. (1988). Science and Medicine in Imperial China—The State of the Field. *The Journal of Asian Studies,* 47(1).

Sivin, N. (1993). Huang ti nei ching 黃帝內經. *In Early Chinese Texts: A Bibliographical Guide,* ed., by M.l Loewe. University of California Press, 196-215.

Sladek, J. (1974). *The New Apocrypha: A Guide to Strange Sciences and Occult Beliefs.* Panther.

Slipher, V. M. (1913). The Radial Velocity of the Andromeda Nebula. *Lowell Observatory Bulletin,* 1, 56–57.

Smoot III, G. (Date unknown) Aristotle's Physics. *Berkeley Lab.* Retrieved March, 2022, from: www.aether.lbl.gov/www/classes/p10/aristotle-physics.html

Spergel, D. (1996, March 6). The Case for Non-Baryonic Matter. *Princeton Department of AstroPhysical Sciences.* Retrieved March, 2022, from: www.astro.princeton.edu/~dns/MAP/Bahcall/node2.html

Spergel, D.N., Et al. (2007). Wilkinson Microwave Anisotropy Probe (WMAP) Three Year Results: Implications for Cosmology (WMAP collaboration). *The Astrophysical Journal Supplement Series*, 170(2), 377–408.

Spottiswood, J. (1997). *Journal of Scientific Exploration*, 11(2), 109-122.

Sridhar, M.K. (2015). The Concept of Jnana, Vijnana and Prajnana According to Vedanta Philosophy. *International Journal of Yoga: Philosophy, Psychology and Parapsychology.*

Standford, R.G., & Stein, A.G. (1994). A Meta-Analysis of ESP Studies Contrasting Hypnosis and Comparison Condition. *Journal of Parapsychology*, 58(3), 235-270.

Steer, I. (2012). Who discovered Universe Expansion?. *Nature*, 490, 176.

Sternheimer, J. (1984). Musique des particules élémentaires: invariance d'échelle, quantification et lois musicales dans la matière. *Compte rendu du Collège de France.*

Sternheimer, J. (1987). Musique des particules élémentaires. *Le Cahier* (Collège International de Philosophie), 180-182.

Stibel J.M. (2021). Decreases in Brain Size and Encephalization in Anatomically Modern Humans. *Brain Behav. Evol.*, 96, 64-77.

Swanson, C. (2003). *The Synchronized Universe*. Poseidia Press.

Swanson, C. (2008). The Torsion Field and the Aura. *Subtle Energies & Energy Medicine Journal Archives*, 19(3), 43.

Swanson, C. (2010). *Life Force: The Scientific Basis*. Poseidia Press.

Targ, R. (1996). Remote Viewing at Stanford Research Institute in the 1970s: A Memoir. *Journal of Scientific Exploration*, 10(I), 77.

Taylor, T. (2010). *The Science Behind the Secret: Decoding the Law of Attraction*. Baen.

Tegmark, M., & Vilenkin, A. (2011). The Case for Parallel Universes. *Scientific American*. Retrieved March, 2022 from: www.scientific-american.com/article/multiverse-the-case-for-parallel-universe/

Templeton A.R. (2010). Has Human Evolution Stopped?. *Rambam Maimonides Medical Journal*, 1(1).

Thaddeus-Johns, J. (2017, January 6). Meet the First Humans to Sense Where North Is. *The Guardian*. Retrieved March, 2022, from: www.theguardian.com/technology/2017/jan/06/first-humans-sense-where-north-is-cyborg-gadget

Thaut, M.H., Altenmüller, E., Finger, S., & Boller, F. (2015). *Progress in Brain Research, Music, Neurology, and Neuroscience: Evolution, the Musical Brain, Medical Conditions, and Therapies*. Elsevier.

Thompson, S.P. (March 23, 1903). *William Gilbert, and Terrestrial Magnetism in the Time of Queen Elizabeth* [Discourse]. Meeting of the Royal Geographical Society, London, England.

Tiller, W. (1992). [Personal communication]. In Swanson, C. (2003). *The Synchronized Universe*. Poseidia Press.

Tiller, W.A., Ph.D. (1997). *Science and Human Transformation: Subtle Energies, Intentionality, and Consciousness*. Pavior Publishing.

Townsend, J.S. (2012). *A Modern Approach to Quantum Mechanics* (2nd ed.). University Science Books.

Toyos, R., McGill, W., & Briscoe, D. (2015). Intense Pulsed Light Treatment for Dry Eye Disease Due to Meibomian Gland Dysfunction: A 3-Year Retrospective Study. *Photomedicine and Laser Surgery*, 33(1), 41–46.

Trapp J., & Jung, M. (2006). The Role of NAD+ Dependent Histone Deacetylases (sirtuins) in Ageing. *Curr. Drug Targets*, 7(11), 1553–1560.

Tuunainen, A., Kripke, D.F., & Endo, T. (2004). Light Therapy for Non-Seasonal Depression. *The Cochrane Database of Systematic Reviews*, 2.

Ullman, M. (1973). Symposium: Psychokinesis on Stable Systems: Work in Progress-PK in the Soviet Union. *Parapsychology Research*, 121-125.

UNEP (United Nations Environment Programme). (2017, February 23). *UN Declares War on Ocean Plastic* [Press release]. www.unep.org/news-and-stories/press-release/un-declares-war-ocean-plastic

Urban, T. (2017, April 20). Neuralink and the Brain's Magical Future. *Wait But Why*. Retrieved March, 2022, from: www.waitbutwhy.com/2017/04/neuralink.html

Utts, J. (1996). An Assessment of the Evidence for Psychic Functioning. *Journal of Scientific Exploration*, 10(1), 3-30.

van Deursen, J.M. (2019). Senolytic Therapies for Healthy Longevity. *Science*, 364(6441), 636–637.

Vassilatos, G. (2000). *Lost Science*. Adventures Unlimited Press.

Voigt, J. (2013). The Man Who Invented "Qigong". Qi: *The Journal of Traditional Eastern Health & Fitness*.

von Bartheld, C.S., Bahney, J., & Herculano-Houzel, S. (2016). The Search for True Numbers of Neurons and Glial Cells in the Human Brain: A Review of 150 Years of Cell Counting. *The Journal of Comparative Neurology*, 524(18), 3865–3895.

von Belkum, S.M., Bosker, F.J., Kortekaas, R., Beersma, D.G.M., & Schoevers, R.A. (2016). Treatment of Depression with Low-Strength Transcranial Pulsed Electromagnetic Fields: A Mechanistic Point of View. *Progress in Neuro-Psychopharmacology and Biological Psychiatry*, 71, 137-143.

von Reichenbach, K.B. (1850). *Researches on Magnetism, Electricity, Heat, Light, Crystallization, and Chemical Attraction in their Relations to The Vital Force*, Parts I and II. W. Gregory (Ed.). Taylor, Walton and Maberly Publishers.

Wang, S.S., Et. al. (2002). New Technology for Deep Light Distribution in Tissue for Phototherapy. *Cancer Journal*, 8(2), 154–163.

Wanjek, C. (Date unknown). Quintessence, Accelerating the Universe?. *Astronomy Today*. Retrieved March, 2022, from: www.astronomytoday.com/cosmology/quintessence.html

Watson, B. (2013). *The Complete Works of Zhuangzi*. Columbia University Press.

Weinberg, S. (2011). *Dreams of a Final Theory: The Scientist's Search for the Ultimate Laws of Nature*. Knopf Doubleday Publishing Group.

Weisskopf, V. (1981). The Development of Field Theory in the Last 50 Years. *Physics Today*, 34(11), 69–85.

Western Electrical Company. (1969). *Fundamentals of Telephone Communication Systems*.

Wetterich, C. (Date unknown). *Quintessence – A Fifth Force from Variation of the Fundamental Scale* [PDF]. Heidelberg University. Retrieved March, 2022, from: www.thphys.uni-heidelberg.de/~wetterich/DEBarcelona0706.pdf

Wheeler, J.A., with Ford, K. (1998). *Geons, Black Holes and Quantum Foam: A Life in Physics.* W.W. Norton.

Whiteman, J.H.M. (1961). *The Mystical Life.* Faber & Faber.

Whitney, Craig R. (1997, August 5). Jeanne Calment, World's Elder, Dies at 122. *The New York Times.*

WHO (World Health Organization). (2014, June). *Antimicrobial resistance: Global Report on Surveillance* [Report]. Retrieved March, 2022, from: www.apps.who.int/iris/bitstream/10665/112642/1/9789241564748_ eng.pdf?ua=1

Wilford, J.N. (1987, December 29). Beyond Gravity: Seeking a Fifth Force, Scientists Find Hints of a Sixth. *The New York Times.*

Will, U., & Berg, E. (2007). Brain Wave Synchronization and Entrainment to Periodic Acoustic Stimuli. *Neurosci Lett.*, 424(1), 55-60.

Williams, E.A. (2003). *A Cultural History of Medical Vitalism in Enlightenment Montpellier.* Ashgate.

Wirz-Justice, A., Daan, S., Folkard, S., Lewy, A., Lund, R., & Zulley, J. (2005). Rutger Wever: An Appreciation. *Journal of Biological Rhythms*, 20(6), 554–555.

Wolf, F.A. (1981). *Taking the Quantum Leap: The New Physics for Non-Scientists.* Harper & Row Publishers.

Woloshyn, T.A. (2017). *"Consuming light". Soaking Up the Rays: Light Therapy and Visual Culture in Britain, C.* 1890-1940. Manchester University Press.

Worm B., Et. al. (2006). Impacts of Biodiversity Loss on Ocean Ecosystem Services. *Science*, 314(5800), 787-790.

Wu, C.Y., Et al. (2015). The Effects of Anti-Dementia and Nootropic Treatments on the Mortality of Patients with Dementia: A Population-Based Cohort Study in Taiwan. *PLoS One*, 10(6).

Yamboliev, I.A., Smyth, L.M., Durnin, L., Dai, Y., & Mutafova-Yambolieva, V.N. (2009). Storage and Secretion of Beta-NAD, ATP and Dopamine in NGF-Differentiated Rat Pheochromocytoma PC12 Cells. *Eur. J.*

Yang, J.M. (1998). *Qigong for Health and Martial Arts: Exercises and Meditation.* YMAA Publication Center.

Yogananda, P. (1946). *Autobiography of a Yogi.* The Philosophical Library, Inc.

Yu, D.; Shuanli, Z; & Hai, D. (2000). "五行阴阳的特征与新英译" [English Translation by Wu X., & Yin, Y.]. *Chinese Journal of Integrative Medicine,* 20(12), 937.

Yu, D.; Shuanli, Z; & Hai, D. (2002). Generalized Quanta Wave with Qi on Traditional Chinese Medicine. *Journal of Mathematical Medicine.*

Xiong, J.H. (2010). *The Outline of Parapsychology* (Revised ed.). University Press of America.

Xu, X. (2000). *Qigong for Treating Common Ailments.* YMAA Publication Center.

Zhavoronkov, A., & Bhuller, B. (2015). Classifying Aging as a Disease in the Context of ICD-11. *Frontiers in Genetics,* 6.

Zumberge, M.A., Et. al. (1990). The Greenland Gravitational Constant Experiment. *Journal of Geophysical Research* (Submitted manuscript), 95(B10).

Zysk, K. (1993). *Religious Medicine: The History and Evolution of Indian Medicine.* Routledge.

Ingram Content Group UK Ltd.
Milton Keynes UK
UKHW021300290623
424274UK00023B/575